SETS, LOGIC, AND AXIOMATIC THEORIES

A SERIES OF UNDERGRADUATES
BOOKS IN MATHEMATICS

R. A. Rosenbaum, EDITOR

Sets, Logic, and Axiomatic Theories

By ROBERT R. STOLL

Oberlin College

W. H. Freeman and Company

SAN FRANCISCO AND LONDON

Preface

This little book has been designed to serve as a textbook for a one-semester course and as a reference book. The subject matter is drawn from that part of mathematics which is commonly called foundations. The term, "foundations of mathematics," holds different meanings for different people. As I use it, I understand an analysis of fundamental concepts of mathematics, intended to serve as a preparation for studying the superstructure from a general and unified perspective. I believe that the material in this book can serve the needs of several groups. One such group is composed of individuals who plan to study some abstract mathematics as undergraduates. If, possibly, there is any distinction, another group consists of those who intend to teach high school mathematics. Another consists of those already teaching mathematics in secondary schools. Finally, I believe that the bright high school student who has become captivated with mathematics can read much of the material with profit. Allow me to defend my contention in conjunction with a description of the topics treated.

Of the textbooks which have appeared in recent years for use in a beginning course in some abstract branch of mathematics, many have a "Chapter 0" outlining prerequisite concepts. Such a chapter is usually inadequate for students encountering these topics for the first time. In this book Chapter 1 is an expanded version of such a Chapter 0, replete with examples and exercises. This, together with the first four sections of Chapter 3, wherein appears a description of the concept of an axiomatic theory as encountered in everyday mathematics, should serve to bridge the gap between an undergraduate's initial conception of mathematics as a computational theory and the abstract nature of more advanced and more modern mathematics. Thus, I argue, mastery of Chapter 1 and the first part of Chapter 3 will enable the undergraduate to start, for example, a first course in topology with topological concepts and a first course in algebra with algebraic concepts without having to devote the first few weeks to discussion of sets, functions, ordering relations, and the like. Persons currently teaching high school mathematics are, of course, familiar with the subject matter under discussion. But they may very well not be familiar with it in its present form and new terminology. That they have this familiarity seems to be essential if they are to be able to read recent articles in journals such as the *Mathematics Teacher*, or to be prepared to teach any one of the new curriculae which have been advanced, or even to evaluate the various new curriculae which have been proposed.

Chapter 2 is devoted to symbolic logic. The simplest part of the standard variety of this subject, namely, the statement calculus, is treated in detail. The restricted predicate calculus, of which the statement calculus is a very small part, is little more than outlined. However, by following the same pattern as that employed for the statement calculus, sufficient momentum should have been gained in the study of the statement calculus to make that of the predicate calculus intelligible. This coverage of symbolic logic is probably adequate for most readers. Further, it does not exceed the minimum coverage, by much, that an educated person should know. Some of the greatest minds have investigated the subject, and their results, when understood, are impressive creations of the human intellect. Every serious student of mathematics should know the elements of symbolic logic, if only to be able to take advantage of its symbolism and learn how to form the negation of "f is continuous at $x = a$."

The final part of Chapter 3 is intended to prepare the reader who wants to learn how symbolic logic comes into play in present-day investigations of questions related to formal axiomatic theories.

Chapter 4 treats the theory of Boolean algebras. This is offered as a reward to those who have struggled through Chapters 1 and 2 and the first part of Chapter 3. Many of the concepts developed are used to obtain, in a small number of pages, a complete picture of the elementary part of a theory which has both historical and current interest. For the icing on the cake I have chosen a theory which is almost embarrassingly rich in structure.

This book constitutes selected portions from a forthcoming, more comprehensive textbook treating the foundations of modern abstract mathematics. Acknowledgments of assistance in what has been prepared so far are numerous. A National Science Foundation Science Faculty Fellowship meshed with a sabbatical leave granted by Oberlin College made it possible for me to devote full time to the project for a year. California Institute of Technology provided a stimulating and refreshing atmosphere in which to work. Further, I am greatly indebted to Professor Angelo Margaris, a former colleague, for aiding my education in matters pertaining to logic. Both Professor Margaris and a reviewer, selected by the publisher, carefully read a preliminary version of the manuscript, pointed out errors, and made numerous suggestions for improvements. Last, but not least, I am grateful to my wife for typing the sequence of successive approximations to the limit and for her patience when I am struggling to write.

September 3, 1960

ROBERT R. STOLL

Contents

Chapter 1

Sets and Relations

THE THEORY OF SETS as a mathematical discipline originated with the German mathematician, G. Cantor (1845–1918). A complete account of its birth and childhood is out of the question here, since a considerable knowledge of mathematics is a prerequisite for its comprehension. Instead, we adopt the uneasy compromise of a brief sketch of these matters. If this proves unsatisfactory to the reader, nothing is lost; on the other hand, if it is at least partially understood, something may be gained.

Cantor's investigation of questions pertaining to trigonometric series and series of real numbers led him to recognize the need for a means of comparing the magnitude of infinite sets of numbers. To cope with this problem, he introduced the notion of the power (or size) of a set by defining two sets to have the *same* power if the members of one can be paired with those of the other. Since two finite sets can be paired if and only if they have the same number of members, the power of a finite set may be identified with a counting number. Thus the notion of power for infinite sets provides a generalization of everyday counting numbers.

1

Cantor developed the theory, including an arithmetic, of these generalized (or transfinite) numbers and in so doing created a theory of sets.
His accomplishments in this area are regarded as an outstanding
example of mathematical creativity.

Cantor's insistence on dealing with the infinite as an actuality—he
regarded infinite sets and transfinite numbers as being on a par with
finite sets and counting numbers—was an innovation at that time.
Prejudices against this viewpoint were responsible for the rejection of
his work by some mathematicians, but others reacted favorably because
the theory provided a proof of the existence of transcendental numbers.
Other applications in analysis and geometry were found, and Cantor's
theory of sets won acceptance to the extent that by 1890 it was recognized as an autonomous branch of mathematics. About the turn of the
century there was some change in attitude with the discovery that
contradictions could be derived within the theory. That these were
not regarded as serious defects is suggested by their being called paradoxes—defects which could be resolved, once full understanding was
acquired. The problems posed by Cantor's theory, together with its
usefulness, gradually created independent interest in a general theory
of abstract sets in which his ideas appeared in greatly extended form.
That general theory forms the basis of this chapter.

Specifically, this chapter discusses, within the framework of set
theory, three important mathematical concepts: function, equivalence
relation, and ordering relation. Sections 1.3–1.6 contain the necessary
preliminaries, and Sections 1.1 and 1.2 describe our point of departure
for Cantor's theory.

One might question the wisdom of choosing a starting point which
is known to ultimately lead to disaster. However, we contend that the
important items of this chapter are independent of those features which
characterize the Cantorian or "naive" approach to set theory. Indeed,
any theory of sets, if it is to serve as a basis for mathematics, will include the principal definitions and theorems appearing in this chapter.
Only the methods we employ to obtain some of these results are naive.
No irreparable harm results in using such methods; they are standard
tools in mathematics.

In this chapter we assume that the reader is familiar with the systems
of integers, rational numbers, real numbers, and complex numbers.
Knowledge in these areas will enlarge the possibilities for constructing

examples to assist the assimilation of definitions, theorems, and so on. We shall reserve the underlined letters $\underline{Z}$, $\underline{Q}$, $\underline{R}$, and $\underline{C}$ for the set of integers, rational numbers, real numbers, and complex numbers, respectively, and the symbols $\underline{Z}^+$, $\underline{Q}^+$, and $\underline{R}^+$ for the set of positive integers, positive rationals, and positive reals, respectively.

1.1. Cantor's Concept of a Set

Let us consider Cantor's concept of the term set and then analyze briefly its constituent parts. According to his definition, a **set** S is any collection of definite, distinguishable objects of our intuition or of our intellect to be conceived as a whole. The objects are called the **elements** or **members** of S.

The essential point of Cantor's concept is that a collection of objects is to be regarded as a single entity (to be conceived as a whole). The transfer of attention from individual objects to collections of individual objects as entities is commonplace, as evidenced by the presence in our language of such words as "bunch," "covey," "pride," and "flock."

With regard to the objects which may be allowed in a set, the phrase, "objects of our intuition or of our intellect," gives considerable freedom. First, it gives complete liberty insofar as the nature of the objects comprising a set is concerned. Green apples, grains of sand, or prime numbers are admissible constituents of sets. However, for mathematical applications it is reasonable to choose as members such mathematical entities as points, lines, numbers, sets of numbers, and so on. Second, it permits the consideration of sets whose members cannot, for one reason or another, be explicitly exhibited. In this connection one is likely to think first of infinite sets, for which it is not even theoretically possible to collect the members as an assembled totality. The set of all prime numbers and the set of all points of the Euclidean plane having rational coordinates in a given coordinate system are examples of this. On the other hand, there are finite sets which display the same degree of intangibility as any infinite set.

An old example which serves to bear out this contention begins with the premise that a typesetting machine with 10,000 characters (these would include the lower-case and capital letters of existing alphabets in various sizes of type, numerals, punctuation, and a blank character for spacing) would be adequate for printing in any language.

(The *exact* size of the set of characters is not at issue; the reader may substitute for 10,000 any integer greater than 1.) Let it be agreed that by a "book" is meant a printed assemblage of 1,000,000 characters, including blank spaces. Thus a book may contain from 0 to 1,000,000 actual characters. Now consider the set of all books. Since there are 10,000 possibilities available for each of the 1,000,000 positions in a book, the total number of books is equal to $10,000^{1,000,000}$. This is a large (but finite!) number. In addition to books of gibberish there would appear in the set all textbooks ever written or planned, all newspapers ever printed, all government pamphlets, all train schedules, all logarithm tables ever computed, and so on, and so on. The magnitude eludes comprehension to the same degree as does that of an infinite set.

The remaining key words in Cantor's concept of a set are "distinguishable" and "definite." The intended meaning of the former, as he used it, was this: With regard to any pair of objects qualified to appear as elements of a particular set, one must be able to determine whether they are different or the same. The attribute "definite" is interpreted as meaning that if given a set and an object, it is possible to determine whether the object is, or is not, a member of the set. The implication is that a set is completely determined by its members.

1.2. The Basis of Intuitive Set Theory

According to Cantor, a set is made up of objects called members or elements (we shall use both terms synonymously). The assumption that if presented with a specific object and a specific set, one can determine whether or not that object is a member of that set means this: If the first blank in "_____ is a member of _____" is filled in with the name of an object, and the second with the name of a set, the resulting sentence is capable of being classified as true or false. Thus, the notion of membership is a relation between objects and sets. We shall symbolize this relation by $\in$ and write

$$x \in A$$

if the object x is a member of the set A. If x is not a member of A, we shall write

$$x \notin A.$$

Further,

$$x_1, x_2, \cdots, x_n \in A$$

will be used as an abbreviation for "$x_1 \in A$ and $x_2 \in A$ and $\cdots$ and $x_n \in A$."

In terms of the membership relation, Cantor's assumption that a set is determined by its members may be stated in the following form.

The intuitive principle of extension. *Two sets are equal iff (if and only if) they have the same members.* The equality of two sets X and Y will be denoted by

$$X = Y,$$

and the inequality of X and Y by

$$X \neq Y.$$

It should be understood that the principle of extension is a nontrivial assumption about the membership relation. In general, a proof of the equality of two specified sets A and B is in two parts: one part demonstrates that if $x \in A$, then $x \in B$; the other demonstrates that if $x \in B$, then $x \in A$. An example of such a proof is given below.

That (uniquely determined) set whose members are the objects $x_1, x_2, \cdots, x_n$ will be written

$$\{x_1, x_2, \cdots, x_n\}.$$

In particular, $\{x\}$, a so-called **unit set,** is the set whose sole member is x.

EXAMPLES A

1. Let us prove that the set A of all positive even integers is equal to the set B of positive integers which are expressible as the sum of two positive odd integers. First we assume that $x \in A$ and deduce that $x \in B$. If $x \in A$, then $x = 2m$, and hence $x = (2m - 1) + 1$, which means that $x \in B$. Next, we assume that $x \in B$ and deduce that $x \in A$. If $x \in B$, then $x = (2p - 1) + (2q - 1)$, and hence $x = 2(p + q - 1)$, which implies that $x \in A$. Thus, we have proved that A and B have the same members.

2. $\{2,4,6\}$ is the set consisting of the first three positive even integers. Since $\{2,4,6\}$ and $\{2,6,4\}$ have the same members, they are equal sets. Moreover, $\{2,4,6\} = \{2,4,4,6\}$ for the same reason.

3. The members of a set may themselves be sets. For instance, the geographical area known as the United States of America is a set of 50 member states, each of which, in turn, is a set of counties. Again, $\{\{1,3\}, \{2,4\}, \{5,6\}\}$ is a set with three members, namely, $\{1,3\}$,

$\{2,4\}$, and $\{5,6\}$. The sets $\{\{1,2\}, \{2,3\}\}$ and $\{1,2,3\}$ are unequal, since the former has $\{1,2\}$ and $\{2,3\}$ as members, and the latter has 1, 2, and 3 as members.

4. The sets $\{\{1,2\}\}$ and $\{1,2\}$ are unequal, since the former, a unit set, has $\{1,2\}$ as its sole member and the latter has 1 and 2 as its members. This is an illustration of the general remark that an object and the set whose sole member is that object are distinct from each other.

We digress briefly to comment on the alphabets which we shall employ in discussing set theory. Usually, lower-case italic English letters will denote elements, and, for the time being, capital italic letters will denote sets which contain them. Later, lower-case Greek letters will be introduced for a certain type of set. If the members of a set are themselves sets, and if this is noteworthy in the discussion, capital script letters will be used for the containing set, and it will be called a **collection of sets.** For example, we might have occasion to discuss the collection $\mathfrak{F}$ of all finite sets A of integers x. As a rule of thumb, the level of a set within a hierarchy of sets under consideration is suggested by the size and gaudiness of the letter employed to denote it.

Although the brace notation is practical for explicitly defining sets made up of a few elements, it is too unwieldly for defining sets having a large, finite number of elements and useless for infinite sets (sets having infinitely many elements). How can sets with a large number of elements be described? In this connection one instinctively tends to differentiate between finite and infinite sets on the grounds that a finite set can be realized as an assembled totality whereas an infinite set cannot. However, a large finite set (for example, the set of books described in Section 1.1) is as incapable of comprehension as is any infinite set. On the basis of such examples one must conclude that the problem of how to describe efficiently a large finite set and the problem of how to describe an infinite set are, for all practical purposes, one and the same.

A commonly accepted solution, devised by Cantor, is based on the concept of a "formula in x." At this time we offer only the following intuitive description. Let us understand by a *statement* a declarative sentence capable of being classified as either true or false. Then, by a formula in x we understand a finite sequence made up from words and the symbol x such that when each occurrence of x is replaced by the same name of an object of an appropriate nature a statement results. For instance, each of the following is a formula in x:

$$5 \text{ divides } x; \qquad x^2 + x + 1 > x;$$
$$x \text{ loves John}; \qquad x^2 = 2.$$
$$x < x;$$

In contrast, neither of the following is a formula in x:

$$\text{for all } x, x^2 - 4 = (x - 2)(x + 2);$$
$$\text{there is an } x \text{ such that } x^2 \leq 0.$$

Rather, each is simply a statement. A grammarian might describe a formula in x, alternatively, as a sentence which asserts something about x. Clearly, each sentence of the first list above has this quality, whereas neither of the second list has. A still different approach to this concept is by way of the notion of function as it is used in elementary mathematics. A formula in x may be described as a function of one variable such that for a suitable domain the function values are statements.

We shall use a capital English letter followed by the symbol (x) to denote a formula in x. If, in a given context, $P(x)$ stands for a particular formula, then $P(a)$ stands for the same formula with a in place of x.

Our objective, that of describing sets in terms of formulas, is achieved by way of the acceptance of the following principle.

The intuitive principle of abstraction. *A formula $P(x)$ defines a set A by the convention that the members of A are exactly those objects a such that $P(a)$ is a true statement.*

Because sets having the same members are equal, a given formula determines exactly one set which, in mathematics, is usually denoted by

$$\{x \mid P(x)\},$$

read "the set of all x such that $P(x)$." Thus $a \in \{x \mid P(x)\}$ iff $P(a)$ is a true statement. It may be said that the decision as to whether a given object a is a member of $\{x \mid P(x)\}$ is that of whether a possesses a certain property (or quality). Because of this, when a formula in x, $P(x)$, is applied to a set construction it is commonly called a *property* of x and, indeed, *the defining property of* $\{x \mid P(x)\}$. Further, our principle of abstraction is then described by the assertion that "every property determines a set."

We shall admit the possibility of the occurrence of symbols other than x in a formula in x. If $P(x)$ is a formula in x and y is a symbol that does not occur in $P(x)$, then, as properties, $P(x)$ and $P(y)$ are indistinguishable, and so $\{x|P(x)\} = \{y|P(y)\}$. This need not be the case, however, if y does occur in $P(x)$. For example,

$$\{x|x \text{ is divisible by } u\} = \{y|y \text{ is divisible by } u\},$$

but

$$\{x|x \text{ is divisible by } u\} \neq \{u|u \text{ is divisible by } u\}.$$

Again, if $F(x)$ and $G(x)$ are two properties such that $F(x)$ holds for x when and only when $G(x)$ holds for x, then $\{x|F(x)\} = \{x|G(x)\}$, by an application of the principle of extension. For example,

$$\{x|x \in A \text{ and } x \in B\} = \{x|x \in B \text{ and } x \in A\},$$

and

$$\{x|x \in \underline{Z}^+ \text{ and } x < 5\} = \{x|x \in \underline{Z}^+ \text{ and } (x + 1)^2 \leq 29\}.$$

EXAMPLES B

1. The introduction of infinite sets by defining properties is a familiar procedure to a student of analytic geometry. One need merely recall the customary definition of such geometric loci as the conic sections. For instance, the circle of radius 2 centered at the origin is the set of all x such that x is a point in the plane and at a distance of two units from the origin.

2. The following are examples of easily recognized sets defined by properties.

(a) $\{x|x \text{ is an integer greater than } 1 \text{ and having no divisors less than or equal to } x^{1/2}\}$.

(b) $\{x|x \text{ is a positive integer less than } 9\}$.

(c) $\{x|x \text{ is a line of slope } 3 \text{ in a coordinate plane}\}$.

(d) $\{x|x \text{ is a continuous function on the closed interval from } 0 \text{ to } 1\}$.

3. $\{x|x = x_1 \text{ or } x = x_2 \text{ or } \cdots \text{ or } x = x_n\}$ is the set we earlier agreed to denote by $\{x_1, x_2, \cdots, x_n\}$.

4. In some cases our language makes possible, by way of a property, a briefer definition of a finite set than can be achieved by an enumeration of the elements. For example, it is shorter to define a particular set of 100 people by the property "x is a senator" than by enumerating names of the members.

5. If A is a set, then $x \in A$ is a formula in x and may be used as a defining property of a set. Since $y \in \{x | x \in A\}$ iff $y \in A$, we have

$$A = \{x | x \in A\},$$

by virtue of the principle of extension.

Various modifications of the basic brace notation for sets are used. For example, it is customary to write

$$\{x \in A | P(x)\}$$

instead of $\{x | x \in A \text{ and } P(x)\}$ for the set of all objects which are both members of A and have property $P(x)$. An alternative description of this set is "all members of A which have property $P(x)$," and it is this description that the new notation emphasizes. As illustrations, $\{x \in \underline{R} | 0 \leq x \leq 1\}$ denotes the set of all real numbers between 0 and 1, inclusive, and $\{x \in \underline{Q}^+ | x^2 < 2\}$ denotes the set of all positive rationals whose square is less than 2.

If $P(x)$ is a property and f is a function, then

$$\{f(x) | P(x)\}$$

will be used to denote the set of all y for which there is an x such that x has property $P(x)$ and $y = f(x)$. For example, instead of writing

$$\{y | \text{ there is an } x \text{ such that } x \text{ is an integer and } y = 2x\}$$

we shall write

$$\{2x | x \in \underline{Z}\}.$$

Again, $\{x^2 | x \in \underline{Z}\}$ denotes the set of squares of integers. Such notations have natural extensions; in general, one's intuition is an adequate guide for interpreting examples. For instance, in a coordinate plane, where the points are identified by the members of the set $\underline{R}^2$ of all ordered pairs $\langle x, y \rangle$† of real numbers x and y, it is reasonable to interpret $\{\langle x, y \rangle \in \underline{R}^2 | y = 2x\}$ as the line through the origin having slope 2.

The principle of set extension, the principle of abstraction, and the principle of choice (which is not formulated until there is need for it) constitute the working basis of Cantor's theory of sets. It is of interest to note that although we made an attempt, prior to introducing the first two principles, to describe what a set *is*, neither of these principles nor the third includes a definition of the word set. Rather, each is

† Here we are using a notation which will be discussed in detail later.

merely an assumption *about* sets. The basic concept used to enunciate these principles is *membership*. Consequently, the membership relation for sets, rather than the notion of set itself, assumes the role of the principal concept of set theory.

We have already mentioned that contradictions can be derived within intuitive set theory. The source of trouble is the *unrestricted* use of the principle of abstraction. Of the known contradictions the simplest to describe is that discovered by Bertrand Russell in 1901. It is associated with the set R having the formula $x \notin x$ as its defining property and may be stated as: On one hand, $R \in R$, and on the other hand, $R \notin R$. The reader can easily supply informal proofs of these two contradictory statements.

EXERCISES

1. Explain why $2 \in \{1,2,3\}$.
2. Is $\{1,2\} \in \{\{1,2,3\}, \{1,3\}, 1,2\}$? Justify your answer.
3. Try to devise a set which is a member of itself.
4. Give an example of sets A, B, and C such that $A \in B$, $B \in C$, and $A \notin C$.
5. Describe in prose each of the following sets.
    (a) $\{x \in \underline{Z} | x$ is divisible by 2 and x is divisible by 3$\}$.
    (b) $\{x | x \in A$ and $x \in B\}$.
    (c) $\{x | x \in A$ or $x \in B\}$.
    (d) $\{x \in \underline{Z}^+ | x \in \{x \in \underline{Z}|$ for some integer y, $x = 2y\}$ and $x \in \{x \in \underline{Z}|$ for some integer y, $x = 3y\}\}$.
    (e) $\{x^2 | x$ is a prime$\}$.
    (f) $\{a/b \in \underline{Q} | a + b = 1$ and $a, b \in \underline{Q}\}$.
    (g) $\{\langle x,y \rangle \in \underline{R}^2 | x^2 + y^2 = 1\}$.
    (h) $\{\langle x,y \rangle \in \underline{R}^2 | y = 2x$ and $y = 3x\}$.
6. Prove that if a, b, c, and d are any objects, not necessarily distinct from one another, then $\{\{a\}, \{a,b\}\} = \{\{c\}, \{c,d\}\}$ iff both $a = c$ and $b = d$.

1.3. Inclusion

We now introduce two further relations for sets. If A and B are sets, then A is **included in** B, symbolized by $A \subseteq B$, iff each member of A is a member of B. In this event one also says that A is a **subset** of B.

Further, we agree that B **includes** A, symbolized by $B \supseteq A$, is synonymous with A is included in B. Thus, $A \subseteq B$ and $B \supseteq A$ each means that, for all x, if $x \in A$, then $x \in B$. The set A is **properly included in** B, symbolized by $A \subset B$ (or, alternatively, A is a **proper subset** of B, and B **properly includes** A), iff $A \subseteq B$ and $A \neq B$. For example, the set of even integers is properly included in the set $\mathbb{Z}$ of integers, and the set $\mathbb{Q}$ of rational numbers properly includes $\mathbb{Z}$.

Among the basic properties of the inclusion relation are the following:

$$X \subseteq X;$$
$$X \subseteq Y \text{ and } Y \subseteq Z \text{ imply } X \subseteq Z;$$
$$X \subseteq Y \text{ and } Y \subseteq X \text{ imply } X = Y.$$

The last of these is the formulation, in terms of the inclusion relation, of the two steps in a proof of the equality of two sets. That is, to prove that $X = Y$, one proves that $X \subseteq Y$ and then that $Y \subseteq X$.

For the relation of proper inclusion, only the analogue of the second property above is valid. The proof that $X \subset Y$ and $Y \subset Z$ imply $X \subset Z$ is required in one of the exercises at the end of this section. There the reader will also find further properties of proper inclusion, insofar as its relationship to inclusion is concerned.

Since beginners tend to confuse the relations of membership and inclusion, we shall take every opportunity to point out distinctions. At this time we note that the analogues for membership of the first two of the above properties for inclusion are false. For example, if X is the set of prime numbers, then $X \notin X$. Again, although $1 \in \mathbb{Z}$ and $\mathbb{Z} \in \{\mathbb{Z}\}$, it is not the case that $1 \in \{\mathbb{Z}\}$, since $\mathbb{Z}$ is the sole member of $\{\mathbb{Z}\}$.

We turn now to a discussion of the subsets of a set, that is, the sets included in a set. This is our first example of an important procedure in set theory—the formation of new sets from an existing set. The principle of abstraction may be used to define subsets of a given set. Indeed, if $P(x)$ is a formula in x and A is a set, then the formula

$$x \in A \text{ and } P(x)$$

determines that subset of A which we have already agreed to write as $\{x \in A | P(x)\}$. If A is a set and we choose $P(x)$ to be $x \neq x$, the result is $\{x \in A | x \neq x\}$, and this set, clearly, has no elements. The principle of extension implies that there can be only one set with no elements. We call this set the **empty set** and symbolize it by

$$\varnothing.$$

The empty set is a subset of every set. To establish this it must be proved that if A is a set, then each member of $\emptyset$ is a member of A. Since $\emptyset$ has no members, the condition is automatically fulfilled. Although this reasoning is correct, it may not be satisfying. An alternative proof which might be more comforting is an indirect one. Assume that it is false that $\emptyset \subseteq A$. This can be the case only if there exists some member of $\emptyset$ which is not a member of A. But this is impossible, since $\emptyset$ has no members. Hence, $\emptyset \subseteq A$ is not false; that is, $\emptyset \subseteq A$.

Each set $A \neq \emptyset$ has at least two distinct subsets, A and $\emptyset$. Moreover, each member of A determines a subset of A; if $a \in A$, then $\{a\} \subseteq A$. There are occasions when one wishes to speak not of individual subsets of a set, but of the set of all subsets of that set. The set of all subsets of a set A is the **power set** of A, symbolized by

$$\mathcal{P}(A).$$

Thus, $\mathcal{P}(A)$ is an abbreviation for

$$\{B | B \subseteq A\}.$$

For instance, if $A = \{1,2,3\}$, then

$$\mathcal{P}(A) = \{A, \{1,2\}, \{1,3\}, \{2,3\}, \{1\}, \{2\}, \{3\}, \emptyset\}.$$

As another instance of the distinction between the membership and inclusion relations we note that if $B \subseteq A$, then $B \in \mathcal{P}(A)$, and if $a \in A$, then $\{a\} \subseteq A$ and $\{a\} \in \mathcal{P}(A)$.

The name "power set of A" for the set of all subsets of A has its origin in the case where A is finite; then $\mathcal{P}(A)$ has 2^n members if A has n members. To prove this, consider the following scheme for describing a subset B of $A = \{a_1, \cdots, a_n\}$: a sequence of n 0's and 1's where the first entry is 1 if $a_1 \in B$ and 0 if $a_1 \notin B$ and where the second entry is 1 if $a_2 \in B$ and 0 if $a_2 \notin B$, and so on. Clearly, the subsets of A can be paired with the set of all such sequences of 0's and 1's; for example, if $n = 4$, then $\{a_1, a_3\}$ determines, and is determined by, the sequence 1010. Since the total number of such sequences is equal to $2 \cdot 2 \cdot \cdots \cdot 2 = 2^n$, the number of elements of $\mathcal{P}(A)$ is equal to 2^n.

EXERCISES

1. Prove each of the following, using any properties of numbers that may be needed.

   (a) $\{x \in \underline{Z}|$ for an integer y, $x = 6y\}$ $=$ $\{x \in \underline{Z}|$ for integers u and v, $x = 2u$ and $x = 3v\}$.
   (b) $\{x \in \underline{R}|$ for a real number y, $x = y^2\}$ $=$ $\{x \in \underline{R}|x \geq 0\}$.
   (c) $\{x \in \underline{Z}|$ for an integer y, $x = 6y\}$ $\subseteq$ $\{x \in \underline{Z}|$ for an integer y, $x = 2y\}$.

2. Prove each of the following for sets A, B, and C.
   (a) If $A \subseteq B$ and $B \subseteq C$, then $A \subseteq C$.
   (b) If $A \subseteq B$ and $B \subset C$, then $A \subset C$.
   (c) If $A \subset B$ and $B \subseteq C$, then $A \subset C$.
   (d) If $A \subset B$ and $B \subset C$, then $A \subset C$.

3. Give an example of sets A, B, C, D, and E which satisfy the following conditions simultaneously: $A \subset B$, $B \in C$, $C \subset D$, and $D \subset E$.

4. Which of the following are true for all sets A, B, and C?
   (a) If $A \not\subseteq B$ and $B \not\subseteq C$, then $A \not\subseteq C$.
   (b) If $A \neq B$ and $B \neq C$, then $A \neq C$.
   (c) If $A \in B$ and $B \not\subseteq C$, then $A \not\subseteq C$.
   (d) If $A \subset B$ and $B \subseteq C$, then $C \not\subseteq A$.
   (e) If $A \subseteq B$ and $B \in C$, then $A \not\subseteq C$.

5. Show that for every set A, $A \subseteq \varnothing$ iff $A = \varnothing$.

6. Let A_1, A_2, $\cdots$, A_n be n sets. Show that

$$A_1 \subseteq A_2 \subseteq \cdots \subseteq A_n \subseteq A_1 \quad \text{iff} \quad A_1 = A_2 = \cdots = A_n.$$

7. Give several examples of a set X such that each element of X is a subset of X.

8. List the members of $\mathcal{P}(A)$ if $A = \{\{1,2\}, \{3\}, 1\}$.

9. For each positive integer n, give an example of a set A_n of n elements such that for each pair of elements of A_n, one member is an element of the other.

1.4. Operations for Sets

We continue with our description of methods for generating new sets from existing sets by defining two methods for composing pairs of sets. These so-called operations for sets parallel, in certain respects, the familiar operations of addition and multiplication for integers. The **union** (**sum, join**) of the sets A and B, symbolized by $A \cup B$ and read "A union B" or "A cup B," is the set of all objects which are members of either A or B; that is,

$$A \cup B = \{x | x \in A \text{ or } x \in B\}.$$

Here the inclusive sense of the word "or" is intended. Thus, by definition, $x \in A \cup B$ iff x is a member of at least one of A and B. For example,

$$\{1,2,3\} \cup \{1,3,4\} = \{1,2,3,4\}.$$

The **intersection** (**product, meet**) of the sets A and B, symbolized by $A \cap B$ and read "A intersection B" or "A cap B," is the set of all objects which are members of both A and B; that is,

$$A \cap B = \{x | x \in A \text{ and } x \in B\}.$$

Thus, by definition, $x \in A \cap B$ iff $x \in A$ and $x \in B$. For example,

$$\{1,2,3\} \cap \{1,3,4\} = \{1,3\}.$$

It is left as an exercise to prove that for every pair of sets A and B the following inclusions hold:

$$\varnothing \subseteq A \cap B \subseteq A \subseteq A \cup B.$$

Two sets A and B are **disjoint** iff $A \cap B = \varnothing$, and they **intersect** iff $A \cap B \neq \varnothing$. A collection of sets is a **disjoint collection** iff each distinct pair of its member sets is disjoint. A **partition** of a set X is a disjoint collection $\mathcal{C}$ of nonempty and distinct subsets of X such that each member of X is a member of some (and, hence, exactly one) member of $\mathcal{C}$. For example, $\{\{1,2\}, \{3\}, \{4,5\}\}$ is a partition of $\{1,2,3,4,5\}$.

A further procedure, that of complementation, for generating sets from existing sets employs a single set. The **absolute complement** of a set A, symbolized by $\overline{A}$, is $\{x | x \notin A\}$. The **relative complement** of A with respect to a set X is $X \cap \overline{A}$; this is usually shortened to $X - A$, read "X minus A." Thus $X - A$ is an abbreviation for

$$\{x \in X | x \notin A\},$$

that is, the set of those members of X which are not members of A. The **symmetric difference** of sets A and B, symbolized by $A + B$, is defined as follows:

$$A + B = (A - B) \cup (B - A).$$

This operation is commutative, that is, $A + B = B + A$, and associative, that is, $(A + B) + C = A + (B + C)$. Further, $A + A = \varnothing$, and $A + \varnothing = A$. Proofs of these statements are left as exercises.

If all sets under consideration in a certain discussion are subsets of a set U, then U is called the **universal set** (for that discussion). As examples, in elementary number theory the universal set is Z, and in plane analytic geometry the universal set is the set of all ordered pairs of real numbers. A graphic device known as a Venn diagram is used for assisting one's thinking on complex relations which may exist among subsets of a universal set U. A Venn diagram is a schematic representation of sets by sets of points: the universal set U is represented by the points within a rectangle, and a subset A of U is represented by the interior of a circle or some other simple region within the rectangle. The complement of A relative to U, which we may abbreviate to $\overline{A}$ without confusion, is the part of the rectangle outside the region repre-

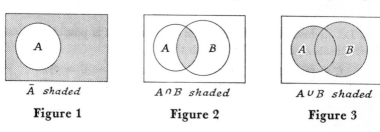

$\overline{A}$ *shaded* $A \cap B$ *shaded* $A \cup B$ *shaded*

Figure 1   **Figure 2**   **Figure 3**

senting A, as shown in Figure 1. If the subsets A and B of U are represented in this way, then $A \cap B$ and $A \cup B$ are represented by shaded regions, as in Figure 2 and Figure 3, respectively. Disjoint sets are represented by nonoverlapping regions, and inclusion is depicted by displaying one region lying entirely within another. These are the ingredients for constructing the Venn diagram of an expression compounded from several sets by means of union, intersection, complementation, and inclusion. The principal applications of Venn diagrams are to problems of simplifying a given complex expression and simplifying given sets of conditions among several subsets of a universe of discourse. Three simple examples of this sort appear below. In many cases such diagrams are inadequate, but they may be helpful in connection with the algebraic approach developed in the next section.

EXAMPLES

1. Suppose A and B are given sets such that $A - B = B - A = \varnothing$. Can the relation of A to B be expressed more simply? Since $A - B = \varnothing$

means $A \cap \overline{B} = \varnothing$, the regions representing A and $\overline{B}$ do not overlap (Figure 4). Clearly, $\overline{\overline{B}} = B$, so we conclude (Figure 5) that $A \subseteq B$. Conversely, if $A \subseteq B$, it is clear that $A - B = \varnothing$. We conclude that $A - B = \varnothing$ iff $A \subseteq B$. Interchanging A and B gives $B - A = \varnothing$ iff $B \subseteq A$. Thus the given relations hold between A and B iff $A \subseteq B$ and $B \subseteq A$ or, $A = B$.

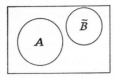

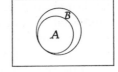

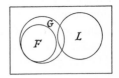

Figure 4   **Figure 5**   **Figure 6**

2. Let us investigate the question of whether it is possible to find three subsets A, B, and C of U such that

$$C \neq \varnothing, A \cap B \neq \varnothing, A \cap C = \varnothing, (A \cap B) - C = \varnothing.$$

The second condition implies that A and B intersect and, therefore, incidentally that neither is empty. From Example 1 the fourth condition amounts to $A \cap B \subseteq C$, from which it follows that the first is superfluous. The associated Venn diagram indicates that A and C intersect; that is, the validity of the second and fourth conditions contradicts the third. Hence, there do not exist sets satisfying all of the conditions simultaneously.

3. Given that F, G, and L are subsets of U such that

$$F \subseteq G, G \cap L \subseteq F, L \cap F = \varnothing.$$

Is it possible to simplify this set of conditions? The Venn diagram (Figure 6) represents only the first and third conditions. The second condition forces L and G to be disjoint, that is, $G \cap L = \varnothing$. On the other hand, if $F \subseteq G$ and $G \cap L = \varnothing$, then all given conditions hold. Thus $F \subseteq G$ and $G \cap L = \varnothing$ constitute a simplification of the given conditions.

EXERCISES

Note: Venn diagrams are *not* to be used in Exercises 1–8.
1. Prove that for all sets A and B, $\varnothing \subseteq A \cap B \subseteq A \cup B$.
2. Let Z be the universal set, and let

$A = \{x \in \mathbf{Z} |$ for some positive integer y, $x = 2y\}$,
$B = \{x \in \mathbf{Z} |$ for some positive integer y, $x = 2y - 1\}$,
$C = \{x \in \mathbf{Z} | x < 10\}$.

Describe $\overline{A}$, $\overline{A \cup B}$, $\overline{C}$, $A - \overline{C}$, and $C - (A \cup B)$ either in prose or by a defining property.

3. Consider the following subsets of $\mathbf{Z}^+$, the set of positive integers:

$A = \{x \in \mathbf{Z}^+ |$ for some integer y, $x = 2y\}$,
$B = \{x \in \mathbf{Z}^+ |$ for some integer y, $x = 2y + 1\}$,
$C = \{x \in \mathbf{Z}^+ |$ for some integer y, $x = 3y\}$.

  (a) Describe $A \cap C$, $B \cup C$, and $B - C$.
  (b) Verify that $A \cap (B \cup C) = (A \cap B) \cup (A \cap C)$.

4. If A is any set, what are each of the following sets? $A \cap \varnothing$, $A \cup \varnothing$, $A - \varnothing$, $A - A$, $\varnothing - A$.

5. Determine $\varnothing \cap \{\varnothing\}$, $\{\varnothing\} \cap \{\varnothing\}$, $\{\varnothing, \{\varnothing\}\} - \varnothing$, $\{\varnothing, \{\varnothing\}\} - \{\varnothing\}$, $\{\varnothing, \{\varnothing\}\} - \{\{\varnothing\}\}$.

6. Suppose A and B are subsets of U. Show that in each of (a), (b), and (c) below if any one of the relations stated holds, then each of the others holds.

  (a) $A \subseteq B$, $\overline{A} \supseteq \overline{B}$, $A \cup B = B$, $A \cap B = A$.
  (b) $A \cap B = \varnothing$, $A \subseteq \overline{B}$, $B \subseteq \overline{A}$.
  (c) $A \cup B = U$, $\overline{A} \subseteq B$, $\overline{B} \subseteq A$.

7. Prove that for all sets A, B, and C,

$$(A \cap B) \cup C = A \cap (B \cup C) \quad \text{iff} \quad C \subseteq A.$$

8. Prove that for all sets A, B, and C,

$$(A - B) - C = (A - C) - (B - C).$$

9. (a) Draw the Venn diagram of the symmetric difference, $A + B$, of sets A and B.
  (b) Using a Venn diagram, show that symmetric difference is a commutative and associative operation.
  (c) Show that for every set A, $A + A = \varnothing$ and $A + \varnothing = A$.

10. The Venn diagram for subsets A, B, and C of U, in general, divides the rectangle representing U into eight nonoverlapping regions. Label each region with a combination of A, B, and C which represents exactly that region.

11. With the aid of a Venn diagram investigate the validity of each of the following inferences:

(a) If A, B, and C are subsets of U such that $A \cap B \subseteq \overline{C}$ and $A \cup C \subseteq B$, then $A \cap C = \varnothing$.

(b) If A, B, and C are subsets of U such that $A \subseteq \overline{B \cup C}$ and $B \subseteq \overline{A \cup C}$, then $B = \varnothing$.

1.5. The Algebra of Sets

If we were to undertake the treatment of problems more complex than those examined above, we would feel the need for more systematic procedures for carrying out calculations with sets related by inclusion, union, intersection, and complementation. That is, what would be called for could appropriately be named "the algebra of sets"—a development of the basic properties of $\cup, \cap, \overline{}$, and $\subseteq$ together with interrelations. As such, the algebra of sets is intended to be the set-theoretic analogue of the familiar algebra of the real numbers, which is concerned with properties of $+$, $\cdot$, and $\leq$ and their interrelations. The basic ingredients of the algebra of sets are various **identities**—equations which are true whatever the universal set U and no matter what particular subsets the letters (other than U and $\varnothing$) represent.

Our first result lists basic properties of union and intersection. For the sake of uniformity, all of these have been formulated for subsets of a universal set U. However, for some of the properties this is a purely artificial restriction, as an examination of the proofs will show.

THEOREM 1.1   For any subsets A, B, C of a set U the following equations are identities. Here $\overline{A}$ is an abbreviation for $U - A$.

1. $A \cup (B \cup C) = (A \cup B) \cup C$.   1'. $A \cap (B \cap C) = (A \cap B) \cap C$.
2. $A \cup B = B \cup A$.   2'. $A \cap B = B \cap A$.
3. $A \cup (B \cap C) = (A \cup B) \cap$ 3'. $A \cap (B \cup C) = (A \cap B) \cup$
   $(A \cup C)$. $(A \cap C)$.
4. $A \cup \varnothing = A$.   4'. $A \cap U = A$.
5. $A \cup \overline{A} = U$.   5'. $A \cap \overline{A} = \varnothing$.

Proof. Each assertion can be verified by showing that the set on either side of the equality sign is included in the set on the other side. As an illustration we shall prove identity 3.

(a) Proof that $A \cup (B \cap C) \subseteq (A \cup B) \cap (A \cup C)$. Let $x \in A \cup (B \cap C)$. Then $x \in A$ or $x \in B \cap C$. If $x \in A$, then $x \in A \cup B$ and

$x \in A \cup C$, and hence x is a member of their intersection. If $x \in B \cap C$, then $x \in B$ and $x \in C$. Hence $x \in A \cup B$ and $x \in A \cup C$, so again x is a member of their intersection.

(b) Proof that $(A \cup B) \cap (A \cup C) \subseteq A \cup (B \cap C)$. Let $x \in (A \cup B) \cap (A \cup C)$. Then $x \in A \cup B$ and $x \in A \cup C$. Hence, $x \in A$, or $x \in B$ and $x \in C$. These imply that $x \in A \cup (B \cap C)$.

Identities 1 and 1′ are referred to as the associative laws for union and intersection, respectively, and identities 2 and 2′ as the commutative laws for these operations. Identities 3 and 3′ are the distributive laws for union and intersection, respectively. The analogy of properties of union and intersection with properties of addition and multiplication, respectively, for numbers, is striking at this point. For instance, 3′ corresponds precisely to the distributive law in arithmetic. That there are also striking differences is illustrated by 3, which has no analogue in arithmetic.

According to the associative law, identity 1, the two sets that can be formed with the operation of union from sets A, B, and C, in that order, are equal. We agree to denote this set by $A \cup B \cup C$. Then the associative law asserts that it is immaterial as to how parentheses are introduced into this expression. Using induction, this result can be generalized to the following. The sets obtainable from given sets A_1, A_2, $\cdots$, A_n, in that order, by use of the operation of union are all equal to one another. The set defined by A_1, A_2, $\cdots$, A_n in this way will be written as

$$A_1 \cup A_2 \cup \cdots \cup A_n.$$

In view of identity 1′ there is also a corresponding generalization for intersection. With these general associative laws on the record we can state the general commutative law: If $1'$, $2'$, $\cdots$, n' are 1, 2, $\cdots$, n in any order, then

$$A_1 \cup A_2 \cup \cdots \cup A_n = A_{1'} \cup A_{2'} \cup \cdots \cup A_{n'};$$

and the general distributive laws:

$$A \cup (B_1 \cap B_2 \cap \cdots \cap B_n) = (A \cup B_1) \cap (A \cup B_2) \cap \cdots \cap (A \cup B_n),$$
$$A \cap (B_1 \cup B_2 \cup \cdots \cup B_n) = (A \cap B_1) \cup (A \cap B_2) \cup \cdots \cup (A \cap B_n).$$

These can also be proved by induction.

Detailed proofs of the foregoing properties of unions and intersections of sets need make no reference to the membership relation; that is, these properties follow solely from those listed in Theorem 1.1. The same is true of those further properties which appear in the next theorem. Such facts may be regarded as the origin of the "axiomatic approach" to the algebra of sets developed in Chapter 4. One derivative of this approach is the conclusion that every theorem of the algebra of sets is derivable from 1–5 and $1'$–$5'$.

These ten properties have another interesting consequence. In Theorem 1.1 they are paired in such a way that each member of a pair is obtainable from the other member by interchanging $\cup$ and $\cap$ and, simultaneously, $\varnothing$ and U. An equation, or an expression, or a statement within the framework of the algebra of sets obtained from another by interchanging $\cup$ and $\cap$ along with $\varnothing$ and U throughout is the **dual** of the original. We contend that the dual of any theorem expressible in terms of $\cup$, $\cap$, and $^{-}$, and which can be proved using only identities 1–5 and $1'$–$5'$, is also a theorem. Indeed, suppose that the proof of such a theorem is written as a sequence of steps and that opposite each step is placed the justification for it. By assumption, each justification is one of 1–5, one of $1'$–$5'$, or a premise of the theorem. Now replace the identity or relation in each step by its dual. Since 1–5 and $1'$–$5'$ contain with each its dual, and the dual of each premise of the original theorem is now a premise, the dual of each justification in the original proof is available to serve as a justification for a step in the new sequence which, therefore, constitutes a proof. The last line of the new sequence is, therefore, a theorem, the dual of the original theorem. Accepting the fact that every theorem of the algebra of sets is deducible from 1–5 and $1'$–$5'$, we then obtain the **principle of duality** for the algebra of sets: If T is any theorem expressed in terms of $\cup$, $\cap$, and $^{-}$, then the dual of T is also a theorem. This implies, for instance, that if the unprimed formulas in the next theorem are deduced solely from Theorem 1.1, then the primed formulas follow by duality. The reader should convince himself that all the assertions in Theorem 1.2 are true by using the definitions of $\cup$, $\cap$, and $^{-}$ in terms of the membership relation. Further, he might try to deduce some of them solely from Theorem 1.1, that is, without appealing in any way to the membership relation. Some demonstrations of this nature appear in the proof of Theorem 4.1.

THEOREM 1.2. For all subsets A and B of a set U, the following statements are valid. Here $\overline{A}$ is an abbreviation for $U - A$.

6. If, for all A, $A \cup B = A$, then $B = \varnothing$.

6'. If, for all A, $A \cap B = A$, then $B = U$.

7, 7'. If $A \cup B = U$ and $A \cap B = \varnothing$, then $B = \overline{A}$.

8, 8'. $\overline{\overline{A}} = A$.

9. $\overline{\varnothing} = U$.

9'. $\overline{U} = \varnothing$.

10. $A \cup A = A$.

10'. $A \cap A = A$.

11. $A \cup U = U$.

11'. $A \cap \varnothing = \varnothing$.

12. $A \cup (A \cap B) = A$.

12'. $A \cap (A \cup B) = A$.

13. $\overline{A \cup B} = \overline{A} \cap \overline{B}$

13'. $\overline{A \cap B} = \overline{A} \cup \overline{B}$.

Some of the identities in Theorem 1.2 have well established names. For example, 10 and 10' are the **idempotent laws,** 12 and 12' are the **absorption laws,** and 13 and 13' the **DeMorgan Laws.** The identities 7, 7' and 8, 8' are each numbered twice to emphasize that each is unchanged by the operation which converts it into its dual; such formulas are called **self-dual.** Note that 7, 7' asserts that each set has a unique complement.

A remark about the form of the next theorem is in order. An assertion of the form, "The statements $R_1, R_2, \cdots, R_k$ are equivalent to one another," means "For all i and j, R_i iff R_j," which, in turn, is the case iff R_1 implies R_2 implies $R_3, \cdots, R_{k-1}$ implies R_k, and R_k implies R_1. The content of the theorem is that the inclusion relation for sets is definable in terms of union as well as in terms of intersection.

THEOREM 1.3. The following statements about sets A and B are equivalent to one another:

(I) $A \subseteq B$;

(II) $A \cap B = A$;

(III) $A \cup B = B$.

Proof. (I) implies (II). Assume that $A \subseteq B$. Since, for all A and B, $A \cap B \subseteq A$, it is sufficient to prove that $A \subseteq A \cap B$. But if $x \in A$, then $x \in B$ and, hence, $x \in A \cap B$. Hence $A \subseteq A \cap B$.

(II) implies (III). Assume $A \cap B = A$. Then $A \cup B = (A \cap B) \cup B = (A \cup B) \cap (B \cup B) = (A \cup B) \cap B = B$.

(III) implies (I). Assume that $A \cup B = B$. Then this and the identity $A \subseteq A \cup B$ imply $A \subseteq B$.

The principle of duality as formulated earlier does not apply directly to expressions in which $-$ or $\subseteq$ appears. One can cope with subtraction by using the unabbreviated form, namely, $A \cap \overline{B}$, for $A - B$. Similarly, by virtue of Theorem 1.3, $A \subseteq B$ may be replaced by $A \cap B = A$ (or $A \cup B = B$). Still better, since the dual of $A \cap B = A$ is $A \cup B = A$, which is equivalent to $A \supseteq B$, the principle of duality may be extended to include the case where the inclusion symbol is present by adding the provision that all inclusion signs be reversed.

EXAMPLES

1. With the aid of the identities now available a great variety of complex expressions involving sets can be simplified, much as in elementary algebra. We give three illustrations.

(a) $\overline{A \cap \overline{B}} \cup B = \overline{A} \cup B \cup B = \overline{A} \cup B.$

(b) $(A \cap B \cap C) \cup (\overline{A} \cap B \cap C) \cup \overline{B} \cup \overline{C}$
$$= [(A \cup \overline{A}) \cap B \cap C] \cup \overline{B} \cup \overline{C}$$
$$= [U \cap B \cap C] \cup \overline{B \cap C}$$
$$= (B \cap C) \cup \overline{B \cap C}$$
$$= U.$$

(c) $(A \cap B \cap C \cap \overline{X}) \cup (\overline{A} \cap C) \cup (\overline{B} \cap C) \cup (C \cap X)$
$$= (A \cap B \cap C \cap \overline{X}) \cup [(\overline{A} \cup \overline{B} \cup X) \cap C]$$
$$= [(A \cap B \cap \overline{X}) \cup \overline{A \cap B \cap \overline{X}}] \cap C$$
$$= U \cap C$$
$$= C.$$

2. There is a theory of equations for the algebra of sets, and it differs considerably from that encountered in high school algebra. As an illustration we shall discuss a method for solving a single equation in one "unknown." Such an equation may be described as one formed using $\cap$, $\cup$, and $\overline{}$ on symbols $A_1, A_2, \cdots, A_n$, and X, where the A's denote fixed subsets of some universal set U and X denotes a subset of U which is constrained only by the equation in which it appears. Using the algebra of sets, the problem is to determine under what conditions such an equation has a solution and then, assuming these are satisfied, to obtain all solutions. A recipe for this follows; the proof required in each step is left as an exercise (see Exercise 7).

Step I. Two sets are equal iff their symmetric difference is equal to $\varnothing$. Hence, an equation in X is equivalent to one whose righthand side is $\varnothing$.

Step II. An equation in X with righthand side $\varnothing$ is equivalent to one of the form

$$(A \cap X) \cup (B \cap \overline{X}) = \varnothing,$$

where A and B are free of X.

Step III. The union of two sets is equal to $\varnothing$ iff each set is equal to $\varnothing$. Hence, the equation in Step II is equivalent to the pair of simultaneous equations

$$A \cap X = \varnothing, \, B \cap \overline{X} = \varnothing.$$

Step IV. The above pair of equations, and hence the original equation, has a solution iff $B \subseteq \overline{A}$. In this event, any X, such that $B \subseteq X \subseteq \overline{A}$, is a solution.

We illustrate the foregoing by deriving necessary and sufficient conditions that the following equation have a solution:

$$X \cup C = D,$$
$$[(X \cup C) \cap \overline{D}] \cup [D \cap (\overline{X \cup C})] = \varnothing, \quad \text{(Step I)}$$
$$[(X \cup C) \cap \overline{D}] \cup [D \cap \overline{X} \cap \overline{C}] = \varnothing,$$
$$(X \cap \overline{D}) \cup (C \cap \overline{D}) \cup (D \cap \overline{X} \cap \overline{C}) = \varnothing,$$
$$(\overline{D} \cap X) \cup [(C \cap \overline{D}) \cap (X \cup \overline{X})] \cup (D \cap \overline{C} \cap \overline{X}) = \varnothing.$$

(The introduction of $X \cup \overline{X}$ in the preceding equation is discussed in Exercise 7.)

$$(\overline{D} \cap X) \cup (C \cap \overline{D} \cap X) \cup (C \cap \overline{D} \cap \overline{X}) \cup (D \cap \overline{C} \cap \overline{X}) = \varnothing,$$
$$\{[\overline{D} \cup (C \cap \overline{D})] \cap X\} \cup \{[(C \cap \overline{D}) \cup (D \cap \overline{C})] \cap \overline{X}\} = \varnothing,$$
$$(\overline{D} \cap X) \cup [(C + D) \cap \overline{X}] = \varnothing, \quad \text{(Step II)}$$
$$\overline{D} \cap X = \varnothing \text{ and } (C + D) \cap \overline{X} = \varnothing. \quad \text{(Step III)}$$

Thus, the original equation has a solution iff

$$C + D \subseteq D. \qquad\qquad \text{(Step IV)}$$

It is left as an exercise to show that this condition simplifies to $C \subseteq D$.

EXERCISES

1. Prove that parts $3'$, $4'$, and $5'$ of Theorem 1.1 are identities.

2. Prove the unprimed parts of Theorem 1.2 using the membership relation. Try to prove the same results using only Theorem 1.1. In at

least one such proof write out the dual of each step to demonstrate that a proof of the dual results.

3. Using only the identities in Theorems 1.1 and 1.2, show that each of the following equations is an identity.

(a) $(A \cap B \cap X) \cup (A \cap B \cap C \cap X \cap Y) \cup (A \cap X \cap \overline{A})$
$= A \cap B \cap X.$

(b) $(A \cap B \cap C) \cup (\overline{A} \cap B \cap C) \cup \overline{B} \cup \overline{C} = U.$

(c) $(A \cap B \cap C \cap \overline{X}) \cup (\overline{A} \cap C) \cup (\overline{B} \cap C) \cup (C \cap X) = C.$

(d) $[(A \cap B) \cup (A \cap C) \cup (\overline{A} \cap \overline{X} \cap Y)] \cap \overline{[(A \cap \overline{B} \cap C) \cup}$
$\overline{(\overline{A} \cap \overline{X} \cap \overline{Y}) \cup (\overline{A} \cap B \cap Y)]} = (A \cap B) \cup (\overline{A} \cap \overline{B} \cap$
$\overline{X} \cap Y).$

4. Rework Exercise 9(b) of Section 1.4 using solely the algebra of sets developed in this section.

5. Let $A_1, A_2, \cdots, A_n$ be sets, and define S_k to be $A_1 \cup A_2 \cup \cdots \cup A_k$ for $k = 1, 2, \cdots, n$. Show that

$$\mathcal{C} = \{A_1, A_2 - S_1, A_3 - S_2, \cdots, A_n - S_{n-1}\}$$

is a disjoint collection of sets and that

$$S_n = A_1 \cup (A_2 - S_1) \cup \cdots \cup (A_n - S_{n-1}).$$

When is $\mathcal{C}$ a partition of S_n?

6. Prove that for arbitrary sets $A_1, A_2, \cdots, A_n (n \geq 2)$,

$A_1 \cup A_2 \cup \cdots \cup A_n = (A_1 - A_2) \cup (A_2 - A_3) \cup \cdots$
$\cup (A_{n-1} - A_n) \cup (A_n - A_1) \cup (A_1 \cap A_2 \cap \cdots \cap A_n).$

7. Referring to Example 2, prove the following:

(a) For all sets A and B, $A = B$ iff $A + B = \varnothing$.

(b) An equation in X with righthand member $\varnothing$ can be reduced to one of the form $(A \cap X) \cup (B \cap \overline{X}) = \varnothing$. (Suggestion: Sketch a proof along these lines. First, apply the DeMorgan laws until only complements of individual sets appear. Then expand the resulting lefthand side by the distributive laws until it is transformed into the union of several terms T_i, each of which is an intersection of several individual sets. Next, if in any T_i neither X nor $\overline{X}$ appears, replace T_i by $T_i \cap (X \cup \overline{X})$ and expand. Finally, group together the terms containing X and those containing $\overline{X}$ and apply the second distributive law.)

(c) For all sets A and B, $A = B = \emptyset$ iff $A \cup B = \emptyset$.

(d) The equation $(A \cap X) \cup (B \cap \overline{X}) = \emptyset$ has a solution iff $B \subseteq \overline{A}$ and then any X such that $B \subseteq X \subseteq \overline{A}$ is a solution.

(e) An alternative form for solutions of the equation in part (d) is $X = (B \cup T) \cap \overline{A}$, where T is an arbitrary set.

8. Show that for arbitrary sets A, B, C, D, and X,

(a) $\overline{[(A \cap X) \cup (B \cap \overline{X})]} = (\overline{A} \cap X) \cup (\overline{B} \cap \overline{X})$;

(b) $[(A \cap X) \cup (B \cap \overline{X})] \cup [(C \cap X) \cup (D \cap \overline{X})]$
$$= [(A \cup C) \cap X] \cup [(B \cup D) \cap \overline{X}];$$

(c) $[(A \cap X) \cup (B \cap \overline{X})] \cap [(C \cap X) \cup (D \cap \overline{X})]$
$$= [(A \cap C) \cap X] \cup [(B \cap D) \cap \overline{X}].$$

9. Using the results in Exercises 7 and 8, prove that the equation

$$(A \cap X) \cup (B \cap \overline{X}) = (C \cap X) \cup (D \cap \overline{X})$$

has a solution iff $B + D \subseteq \overline{A + C}$. In this event determine all solutions.

1.6. Relations

In mathematics the word "relation" is used in the sense of relationship. The following partial sentences (or predicates) are examples of relations:

is less than,	is included in,
divides,	is a member of,
is congruent to,	is the mother of.

In this section the concept of a relation will be developed within the framework of set theory. The motivation for the forthcoming definition is this: A (binary) relation is used in connection with pairs of objects considered in a definite order. Further, a relation is concerned with the existence or nonexistence of some type of bond between certain ordered pairs. We infer that a relation provides a criterion for distinguishing some ordered pairs from others in the following sense. If a list of all ordered pairs for which the relation is pertinent is available, then with each may be associated "yes" or "no" to indicate that a pair is or is not in the given relation. Clearly, the same end is achieved by listing exactly all those pairs which are in the given relation. Such a list characterizes the relation. Thus the stage is set for defining a relation as a set of ordered pairs, and this is done as soon as the notion of an ordered pair is made precise.

Intuitively, an ordered pair is simply an entity consisting of two objects in a specified order. As the notion is used in mathematics, one relies on ordered pairs to have two properties: (i) given any two objects, x and y, there exists an object, which might be denoted by $\langle x,y \rangle$ and called the ordered pair of x and y, that is uniquely determined by x and y; (ii) if $\langle x,y \rangle$ and $\langle u,v \rangle$ are two ordered pairs, then $\langle x,y \rangle = \langle u,v \rangle$ iff $x = u$ and $y = v$. Now it is possible to define an object, indeed, a set, which has these properties: the **ordered pair** of x and y, symbolized by $\langle x,y \rangle$, is

$$\{\{x\}, \{x,y\}\},$$

that is, the two-element set one of whose members, $\{x,y\}$, is the un-ordered pair involved, and the other, $\{x\}$, determines which member of this unordered pair is to be considered as being "first." We shall now prove that, as defined, ordered pairs have the properties mentioned above.

THEOREM 1.4.   The ordered pair of x and y is uniquely deter-mined by x and y. Moreover, if $\langle x,y \rangle = \langle u,v \rangle$, then $x = u$ and $y = v$.

Proof.   That x and y uniquely determine $\langle x,y \rangle$ follows from our assumption that a set is uniquely determined by its members. Turn-ing to the more profound part of the proof, let us assume that $\langle x,y \rangle = \langle u,v \rangle$. We consider two cases:

(I) $u = v$. Then $\langle u,v \rangle = \{\{u\},\{u,v\}\} = \{\{u\}\}$. Hence $\{\{x\}, \{x,y\}\}$ $= \{\{u\}\}$, which implies that $\{x\} = \{x,y\} = \{u\}$ and, in turn, that $x = u$ and $y = v$.

(II) $u \neq v$. Then $\{u\} \neq \{u,v\}$ and $\{x\} \neq \{u,v\}$. Since $\{x\} \in \{\{u\}, \{u,v\}\}$, it follows that $\{x\} = \{u\}$ and, hence, $x = u$. Since $\{u,v\} \in \{\{x\}, \{x,y\}\}$ and $\{u,v\} \neq \{x\}$, we have $\{u,v\} = \{x,y\}$. Thus, $\{x\} \neq \{x,y\}$, so, in turn, $x \neq y$ and $y \neq u$. Hence $y = v$.

We call x the **first coordinate** and y the **second coordinate** of the ordered pair $\langle x,y \rangle$. Ordered triples and, in general, ordered n-tuples may be defined in terms of ordered pairs. The **ordered triple** of x, y and z, symbolized by $\langle x,y,z \rangle$, is defined to be the ordered pair $\langle \langle x,y \rangle, z \rangle$. Assuming that ordered $(n-1)$-tuples have been defined, we take the

ordered n-tuple of x_1, x_2, $\cdots$, x_n, symbolized by $\langle x_1, x_2, \cdots, x_n \rangle$, to be $\langle \langle x_1, x_2, \cdots, x_{n-1} \rangle, x_n \rangle$.

We return to our principal topic by defining a **binary relation** as a set of ordered pairs, that is, a set each of whose members is an ordered pair. If ρ is a relation, we write $\langle x,y \rangle \in \rho$ and $x\rho y$ interchangeably, and we say that x is ρ-**related to** y iff $x\rho y$. There are established symbols for various relations such as equality, membership, inclusion, congruence. Such familiar notation as $x = y$, $x < y$, and $x \equiv y$ is the origin of $x\rho y$ as a substitute for "$\langle x,y \rangle \in \rho$."

A natural generalization of a binary relation is that of an n-**ary relation** as a set of ordered n-tuples. The case $n = 2$ is, of course, the one for which we have agreed on the name "binary relation." Similarly, in place of 3-ary relation we shall say **ternary relation.**

EXAMPLES A

1. $\{\langle 2,4 \rangle, \langle 7,3 \rangle, \langle 3,3 \rangle, \langle 2,1 \rangle\}$ as a set of ordered pairs is a binary relation. The fact that it appears to have no particular significance suggests that it is not worthwhile assigning a name to.

2. The relation "less than" for integers is $\{\langle x,y \rangle |$ for integers x and y, there is a positive integer z for which $x + z = y\}$. Symbolizing this relation in the traditional way, the statements "$2 < 5$" and "$\langle 2,5 \rangle \in <$" are synonymous (and true).

3. If μ symbolizes the relation of motherhood, then $\langle$Jane, John$\rangle \in \mu$ means that Jane is the mother of John.

4. Human parenthood is an example of a ternary relation. If it is symbolized by ρ, then $\langle$Elizabeth, Philip, Charles$\rangle \in \rho$ indicates that Elizabeth and Philip are the parents of Charles. Addition in $\mathbb{Z}$ is another ternary relation; writing "$5 = 2 + 3$" may be considered as an alternative to asserting that $\langle 5,2,3 \rangle \in +$.

5. The cube root relation for real numbers is $\{\langle x^{1/3},x \rangle | \ x \in \mathbb{R}\}$. One member of this relation is $\langle 2,8 \rangle$.

6. In trigonometry the sine function is defined by way of a rule for associating with each real number a real number between -1 and 1. In practical applications one relies on a table in a handbook for values of this function for various arguments. Such a table is simply a compact way of displaying a set of ordered pairs. Thus, for practical purposes, the sine function is defined by the set of ordered pairs exhibited in a table (together with a rule concerning the extension of the table). We

note that as such a table is designed to be read it presents pairs of the form $\langle x, \sin x \rangle$; thereby the coordinates are interchanged from the order in which we have been writing them for relations in general. That is, for an arbitrary relation ρ we have interpreted $\langle a,b \rangle \in \rho$ as meaning that a is ρ-related to b, whereas the presence of $\langle \pi/2, 1 \rangle$ in a table for the sine function is intended to convey the information that the second coordinate is sine-related (is the sine of) the first coordinate.

Later we shall find extensive applications for ternary relations, but our present interest is in binary relations, which we shall abbreviate to simply "relations" if no confusion can result. If ρ is a relation, then the **domain** of ρ, symbolized by D_ρ, is

$$\{x | \text{for some } y, \langle x,y \rangle \in \rho\},$$

and the **range** of ρ, symbolized by R_ρ, is

$$\{y | \text{ for some } x, \langle x,y \rangle \in \rho\}.$$

That is, the domain of ρ is the set whose members are the first coordinates of members of ρ, and the range of ρ is the set whose members are the second coordinates of members of ρ. For example, the domain and range of the inclusion relation for subsets of a set U are each equal to $\mathcal{P}(U)$. Again, the domain of the relation of motherhood is the set of all mothers, and the range is the set of all people.

One of the simplest types of relations is the set of all pairs $\langle x,y \rangle$, such that x is a member of some fixed set X and y is a member of some fixed set Y. This relation is the **cartesian product,** $X \times Y$, of X and Y. Thus,

$$X \times Y = \{\langle x,y \rangle | x \in X \text{ and } y \in Y\}.$$

It is evident that a relation ρ is a subset of any cartesian product $X \times Y$, such that $X \supseteq D_\rho$ and $Y \supseteq R_\rho$. If ρ is a relation and $\rho \subseteq X \times Y$, then ρ is referred to as a **relation from** X **to** Y. If ρ is a relation from X to Y and $Z \supseteq X \cup Y$, then ρ is a relation from Z to Z. A relation from Z to Z will be called a **relation in** Z. Such terminologies as "a relation from X to Y" and "a relation in Z" stem from the possible application of a relation to distinguish certain ordered pairs of objects from others. If X is a set, then $X \times X$ is a relation in X which we shall call the **universal relation** in X; this is a suggestive name, since, for each pair x,y of elements in X, we have $x(X \times X)y$. At the other extreme is the

void relation in X, consisting of the empty set. Intermediate is the **identity relation** in X, symbolized by ι or ι_X, which is $\{\langle x,x \rangle | x \in X\}$. For x,y in X, clearly, $x \iota_X y$ iff $x = y$.

If ρ is a relation and A is a set, then $\rho[A]$ is defined to be

$$\{y | \text{ for some } x \text{ in } A, \; x\rho y\}.$$

This set is suggestively called the set of ρ-**relatives** of elements of A. Clearly, $\rho[D_\rho] = R_\rho$, and, if A is any set, $\rho[A] \subseteq R_\rho$.

EXAMPLES B

1. If $Y \neq \varnothing$, then $D_{X \times Y} = X$, and if $X \neq \varnothing$, then $R_{X \times Y} = Y$.

2. The basis for plane analytic geometry is the assumption that the points of the Euclidean plane can be paired with the members of $\underset{\sim}{R} \times \underset{\sim}{R}$, the set of ordered pairs of real numbers. Thereby the study of plane geometric configurations may be replaced by that of subsets of $\underset{\sim}{R} \times \underset{\sim}{R}$, that is, relations in $\underset{\sim}{R}$. For geometric configurations which are likely to be of interest, one can anticipate that the defining property of the associated relation in $\underset{\sim}{R}$ will be an algebraic equation in x and y, or an inequality involving x and y, or some combination of equations and inequalities. In this event it is standard practice to take the defining property of the relation associated with a configuration as a description of the configuration and omit any explicit mention of the relation. For example, "the line with equation $y = 2x + 1$" is shorthand for "the set of points which are associated with $\{\langle x,y \rangle \in \underset{\sim}{R} \times \underset{\sim}{R} | y = 2x + 1\}$." Again, "the region defined by $y < x$" is intended to refer to the set of points associated with $\{\langle x,y \rangle \in \underset{\sim}{R} \times \underset{\sim}{R} | y < x\}$. As a further example,

$$x \leq 0 \text{ and } y \geq 0 \text{ and } y \leq 2x + 1$$

serves as a definition of a triangle-shaped region in the plane, as the reader can verify.

If relations in $\underset{\sim}{R}$, instead of sets of points in the plane, are the primary objects of study, then the set of points corresponding to the members of of a relation is called the **graph** of the relation (or of the defining property of the relation). Below appear four relations, and above each is sketched its graph. When the graph includes a region of the plane, this is indicated by shading.

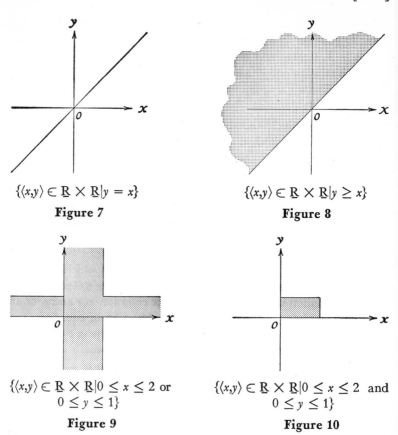

$\{\langle x,y \rangle \in \underline{R} \times \underline{R} | y = x\}$

Figure 7

$\{\langle x,y \rangle \in \underline{R} \times \underline{R} | y \geq x\}$

Figure 8

$\{\langle x,y \rangle \in \underline{R} \times \underline{R} | 0 \leq x \leq 2 \text{ or } 0 \leq y \leq 1\}$

Figure 9

$\{\langle x,y \rangle \in \underline{R} \times \underline{R} | 0 \leq x \leq 2 \text{ and } 0 \leq y \leq 1\}$

Figure 10

If ρ is the relation in $\underline{R}$ with $0 \leq x \leq 2$ as defining property and σ is the relation in $\underline{R}$ with $0 \leq y \leq 1$ as defining property, then the relation accompanying Figure 9 is equal to $\rho \cup \sigma$, and the relation accompanying Figure 10 is $\rho \cap \sigma$. Thus, Figures 9 and 10 illustrate the remarks that the graph of the union of two relations, ρ and σ, is the union of the graph of ρ and the graph of σ, and the graph of $\rho \cap \sigma$ is the intersection of the graphs of ρ and σ.

3. Let ρ be the relation "is the father of." If A is the set of all men now living in the United States, then $\rho[A]$ is the set of all people whose fathers now live in the United States. If $A = \{\text{Adam, Eve}\}$, then $\rho[A] = \{\text{Cain, Abel}\}$.

EXERCISES

1. Show that if $\langle x,y,z \rangle = \langle u,v,w \rangle$, then $x = u$, $y = v$, and $z = w$.

2. Write the members of $\{1,2\} \times \{2,3,4\}$. What are the domain and range of this relation? What is its graph?

3. State the domain and the range of each of the following relations, and then draw its graph.

    (a) $\{\langle x,y \rangle \in \underline{R} \times \underline{R} \mid x^2 + 4y^2 = 1\}$.
    (b) $\{\langle x,y \rangle \in \underline{R} \times \underline{R} \mid x^2 = y^2\}$.
    (c) $\{\langle x,y \rangle \in \underline{R} \times \underline{R} \mid |x| + 2\,|y| = 1\}$.
    (d) $\{\langle x,y \rangle \in \underline{R} \times \underline{R} \mid x^2 + y^2 < 1 \text{ and } x > 0\}$.
    (e) $\{\langle x,y \rangle \in \underline{R} \times \underline{R} \mid y \geq 0 \text{ and } y \leq x \text{ and } x + y \leq 1\}$.

4. Write the relation in Exercise 3(c) as the union of four relations and that in Exercise 3(e) as the intersection of three relations.

5. The formation of the cartesian product of two sets is a binary operation for sets. Show by examples that this operation is neither commutative nor associative.

6. Let β be the relation "is a brother of," and let σ be the relation "is a sister of." Describe $\beta \cup \sigma$, $\beta \cap \sigma$, and $\beta - \sigma$.

7. Let β and σ have the same meaning as in Exercise 6. Let A be the set of students now in the reader's school. What is $\beta[A]$? What is $(\beta \cup \sigma)[A]$?

8. Prove that if A, B, C, and D are sets, then $(A \cap B) \times (C \cap D) = (A \times C) \cap (B \times D)$. Deduce that the cartesian multiplication of sets distributes over the operation of intersection, that is, that $(A \cap B) \times C = (A \times C) \cap (B \times C)$ and $A \times (B \cap C) = (A \times B) \cap (A \times C)$ for all A, B, and C.

9. Exhibit four sets A, B, C, and D for which $(A \cup B) \times (C \cup D) \neq (A \times C) \cup (B \times D)$.

10. In spite of the result in the preceding exercise, cartesian multiplication distributes over the operation of union. Prove this.

11. Investigate whether union and intersection distribute over cartesian multiplication.

12. Prove that if A, B, and C are sets such that $A \neq \varnothing$, $B \neq \varnothing$, and $(A \times B) \cup (B \times A) = C \times C$, then $A = B = C$.

1.7. Equivalence Relations

A relation ρ in a set X is **reflexive** if $x\rho x$ for each x in X; it is **symmetric** if $x\rho y$ implies $y\rho x$; and it is **transitive** if $x\rho y$ and $y\rho z$ imply $x\rho z$. Relations having these three properties occur so frequently in mathematics they have acquired a name. A relation in a set is an **equivalence relation** if it is reflexive, symmetric, and transitive. If the relation ρ in X is an equivalence relation, then it is clear that $D_\rho = X$. Because of this we shall henceforth use the terminology "an equivalence relation on X" for a relation which is an equivalence relation in X.

EXAMPLES A

Each of the following relations is an equivalence relation on the accompanying set.

1. Equality in a collection of sets.

2. The geometric notion of similarity in the set of all triangles of the Euclidean plane.

3. The relation of congruence modulo n in $\mathbb{Z}$. This relation is defined for a nonzero integer n as follows: x is congruent to y, symbolized $x \equiv y \pmod{n}$, iff n divides $x - y$.

4. The relation $\sim$ in the set of all ordered pairs of positive integers where $\langle x,y \rangle \sim \langle u,v \rangle$ iff $xv = yu$.

5. The relation of parallelism in the set of lines in the Euclidean plane.

6. The relation of having the same number of members in a collection of finite sets.

7. The relation of "living in the same house" in the set of people of the United States.

The last example above illustrates, in familiar terms, the central feature of any equivalence relation: It divides the population into disjoint subsets, in this case the sets of people who live in the same house. Let us establish our contention in general. If ρ is an equivalence relation on the set X, then a subset A of X is an **equivalence class** (ρ-equivalence class) iff there is a member x of A such that A is equal to the set of all y for which $x\rho y$. Thus, A is an equivalence class iff there exists an x in X such that $A = \rho[\{x\}]$. If there is no ambiguity about the relation at hand, the set of all ρ-relatives of x in X will be abbreviated $[x]$ and called the equivalence class generated by x. Two basic properties of equivalence classes are the following:

  (I) $x \in [x]$;

  (II) if $x\rho y$, then $[x] = [y]$.

The first is a consequence of the reflexivity of an equivalence relation. To prove the second, assume that $x\rho y$. Then $[y] \subseteq [x]$ since $z \in [y]$ (which means that $y\rho z$) together with $x\rho y$ and the transitivity of ρ yield $x\rho z$ or $z \in [x]$. The symmetry of ρ may be used to conclude the reverse inclusion, and the equality of $[x]$ and $[y]$ follows.

Now property (I) implies that each member of X is a member of an equivalence class, and (II) implies that two equivalence classes are either disjoint or equal since if $z \in [x]$ and $z \in [y]$, then $[x] = [z]$, $[y] = [z]$, and hence $[x] = [y]$. Recalling the definition of a partition of a nonempty set, we conclude that the collection of distinct ρ-equivalence classes is a partition of X. This proves the first assertion in the following theorem.

THEOREM 1.5.   Let ρ be an equivalence relation on X. Then the collection of distinct ρ-equivalence classes is a partition of X. Conversely, if $\mathcal{P}$ is a partition of X, and a relation ρ is defined by $a\rho b$ iff there exists A in $\mathcal{P}$ such that $a, b \in A$, then ρ is an equivalence relation on X. Moreover, if an equivalence relation ρ determines the partition $\mathcal{P}$ of X, then the equivalence relation defined by $\mathcal{P}$ is equal to ρ. Conversely, if a partition $\mathcal{P}$ of X determines the equivalence relation ρ, then the partition of X defined by ρ is equal to $\mathcal{P}$.

Proof.   To prove the second statement, let $\mathcal{P}$ be a partition of X. The relation ρ which is proposed is symmetric from its definition. If $a \in X$, there exists A in $\mathcal{P}$ with $a \in A$, so that ρ is reflexive. To show the transitivity of ρ, assume that $a\rho b$ and $b\rho c$. Then there exists A in $\mathcal{P}$ with $a, b \in A$, and there exists B in $\mathcal{P}$ with $b, c \in B$. Since $b \in A$ and $b \in B$, $A = B$. Hence $a\rho c$.

To prove the next assertion, assume that an equivalence relation ρ on X is given, that it determines the partition $\mathcal{P}$ of X and, finally, that $\mathcal{P}$ determines the equivalence relation $\rho *$. We show that $\rho = \rho *$. Assume that $\langle x, y \rangle \in \rho$. Then $x, y \in [x]$ and $[x] \in \mathcal{P}$. By virtue of the definition of $\rho *$ it follows that $x\rho *y$ or $\langle x, y \rangle \in \rho *$. Conversely, given

$\langle x, y \rangle \in \rho^*$, there exists A in $\mathcal{P}$ with $x, y \in A$. But A is a ρ-equivalence class, and hence $x \rho y$ or $\langle x, y \rangle \in \rho$. Thus, $\rho = \rho^*$.

The last part of the theorem is left as an exercise.

To illustrate part of the above theorem let us examine the equivalence relation of congruence modulo n on $\underline{Z}$ which was defined in the third of Examples A. An equivalence class consists of all numbers $a + kn$ with k in $\underline{Z}$. Clearly, therefore, $[0], [1], \cdots, [n-1]$ are distinct classes. There are no others, since any integer a can be written in the form $a = qn + r$, $0 \leq r < n$, and hence $a \in [r]$. A class of congruent numbers is often called a **residue class** modulo n. The collection of residue classes modulo n will be denoted by $\underline{Z}_n$. We can use this example to emphasize the fact that, for any equivalence relation ρ, an equivalence class is defined by any one of its members, since if $x \rho y$, then $[x] = [y]$. Thus, $[0] = [n] = [2n]$, and so on, and $[1] = [n+1] = [1-n]$, and so on.

If ρ is an equivalence relation on X, we shall denote the partition of X induced by ρ by X/ρ (read "X modulo ρ") and call it the **quotient set** of X by ρ. The significance of the partition of a set X accompanying an arbitrary equivalence relation ρ on X is best realized by comparing ρ with the extreme equivalence relation on X of identity. We classify identity on X as an extreme equivalence relation because the only element equal to a given element is itself. That is, the partition of X determined by identity is the finest possible—the equivalence class generated by x consists of x alone. In contrast, for two elements to be ρ-equivalent they must merely have a single likeness in common, namely, that characterized by ρ. A ρ-equivalence class consists of all elements of X which are indiscernible with respect to ρ. That is, an arbitrary equivalence relation on X defines a generalized form of equality on X. On turning from the elements of X to the ρ-equivalence classes we have the effect of identifying any two elements which are ρ-equivalent. If ρ happens to preserve various structural features of X (assuming it has such), these may appear in simplified form in X/ρ because of the identification of elements which accompanies the transition to X/ρ. Examples of this arise quite naturally later.

Among the applications of equivalence relations in mathematics is that of formalizing mathematical notions or, as one often says, formulating definitions by abstraction. The essence of this technique is defining a notion as the set of all objects which one intends to have qualify for the notion. This seems incestuous on the surface, but in practice it serves very nicely. For example, let us consider the problem of defining the positive rational numbers in terms of the positive integers. Instead of defining ratios of integers directly we introduce the notion of pairs of integers having equal ratios by the definition $\langle x,y \rangle \sim \langle u,v \rangle$ iff $xv = yu$. This is an equivalence relation on $\underline{Z}^+ \times \underline{Z}^+$, and we can now define a rational number as an equivalence class. That is, the notion of equivalence of pairs of integers amounts to imposing a criteria for indiscernibility on $\underline{Z}^+ \times \underline{Z}^+$. Since this is an equivalence relation, a partition of the universe of discourse is at hand, and in an equivalence class we have the abstraction of the property common to all of its members. Thus we define a rational number to be such an equivalence class. The familiar symbol x/y emerges as an abbreviation for the equivalence class $[\langle x,y \rangle]$. That an equivalence class is defined by each of its members implies that any other symbol u/v, where $\langle u,v \rangle \in [\langle x,y \rangle]$, may be taken as a name for the same rational number. For example, the statement $2/3 = 4/6$ is true because $2/3$ and $4/6$ are names for the same rational number.

Another instance of definition by abstraction is that of direction based on the equivalence relation of parallelism: a direction is an equivalence class of parallel rays. The notion of shape may be conceived in a like fashion: geometric similarity is an equivalence relation on the set of figures in the Euclidean plane, and a shape may be defined as an equivalence class under similarity.

So far, the fundamental result concerning an equivalence relation ρ—that the collection of all distinct ρ-equivalence classes is disjoint and $x\rho y$ iff x and y are members of the same equivalence class—has been employed solely in connection with applications of equivalence relations. It can also be made the basis of a characterization of equivalence relations among relations in general. This is done next.

THEOREM 1.6. A relation ρ is an equivalence relation iff there exists a disjoint collection $\mathcal{P}$ such that

$$\rho = \{\langle x,y \rangle | \text{ for some } C \text{ in } \mathcal{P}, \langle x,y \rangle \in C \times C\}.$$

Proof. Assume that ρ is an equivalence relation on X. Then the collection of distinct ρ-equivalence classes is disjoint, and we contend that with this choice for $\mathcal{P}$, ρ has the structure described in the theorem. We show first that $\{\langle x,y \rangle|$ for some C in $\mathcal{P}$, $\langle x,y \rangle \in C \times C\}$ $\subseteq \rho$. Assume that $\langle x,y \rangle$ is a member of the set on the left side of the inclusion sign. Then there exists an equivalence class $[z]$ with x, $y \in [z]$. Then $z\rho x$ and $z\rho y$, and hence $x\rho y$, which means that $\langle x,y \rangle \in \rho$. To show the reverse inclusion, assume that $\langle x,y \rangle \in \rho$. Then x, $y \in [x]$, and hence $\langle x,y \rangle \in [x] \times [x]$.

The proof of the converse is straightforward and is left as an exercise.

EXERCISES

1. If ρ is a relation in $\underline{R}^+$, then its graph is a set of points in the first quadrant of a coordinate plane. What is the characteristic feature of such a graph if: (a) ρ is reflexive, (b) ρ is symmetric, (c) ρ is transitive?

2. Using the results of Exercise 1, try to formulate a compact characterization of the graph of an equivalence relation on $\underline{R}^+$.

3. The collection of sets $\{\{1,3,4\}, \{2,7\}, \{5,6\}\}$ is a partition of $\{1,2,3,4,5,6,7\}$. Draw the graph of the accompanying equivalence relation.

4. Let ρ and σ be equivalence relations. Prove that $\rho \cap \sigma$ is an equivalence relation.

5. Prove that ρ is an equivalence relation on a set Y iff $\rho \cap (Y \times Y)$ is an equivalence relation with domain Y.

6. Give an example of:
    (a) a relation which is reflexive and symmetric but not transitive in some set;
    (b) a relation which is reflexive and transitive but not symmetric in some set;
    (c) a relation which is symmetric and transitive but not reflexive in some set.

7. Complete the proof of Theorem 1.5.

8. Each equivalence relation on a set X defines a partition of X according to Theorem 1.5. What equivalence yields the finest partition? The coarsest partition?

9. Complete the proof of Theorem 1.6.

10. Let ρ be a relation which is reflexive and transitive in the set A. For $a, b \in A$, define $a \sim b$ iff $a\rho b$ and $b\rho a$.
    (a) Show that $\sim$ is an equivalence relation on A.

    (b) For $[a],[b] \in A/\sim$, define $[a]\rho'[b]$ iff $a\rho b$. Show that this definition is independent of a and b in the sense that if $a' \in [a]$, $b' \in [b]$, and $a\rho b$, then $a'\rho b'$.

    (c) Show that ρ' is reflexive and transitive. Further, show that if $[a]\rho'[b]$ and $[b]\rho'[a]$, then $[a] = [b]$.

11. In the set $Z^+ \times Z^+$ define $\langle a,b \rangle \sim \langle c,d \rangle$ iff $a + d = b + c$. Show that $\sim$ is an equivalence relation on this set. Indicate the graph of $Z^+ \times Z^+$, and describe the $\sim$-equivalence classes.

1.8. Functions

It is possible to define the concept of function in terms of notions already introduced. Such a definition is based on the common part of the discussions about functions to be found in many elementary texts, namely, the definition of the graph of a function as a set of ordered pairs. Once it is recognized that there is no information about a function which cannot be derived from its graph, there is no need to distinguish between a function and its graph. As such, it is reasonable to base a definition on just that feature of a set of ordered pairs which would qualify it to be a graph of a function. This we do by agreeing that a **function** is a relation such that no two distinct members have the same first coordinate. Thus, f is a function iff it meets the following requirements:

    (I) The members of f are ordered pairs.

    (II) If $\langle x,y \rangle$ and $\langle x,z \rangle$ are members of f, then $y = z$.

EXAMPLES A

1. $\{\langle 1,2 \rangle, \langle 2,2 \rangle, \langle \text{Roosevelt, Churchill} \rangle\}$ is a function with domain $\{1,2, \text{Roosevelt}\}$ and range $\{2, \text{Churchill}\}$.

2. The relation $\{\langle 1,2 \rangle, \langle 1,3 \rangle, \langle 2,2 \rangle\}$ is not a function, since the distinct members $\langle 1,2 \rangle$ and $\langle 1,3 \rangle$ have the same first coordinate.

3. The relation $\{\langle x, x^2 + x + 1 \rangle | x \in R\}$ is a function, because if $x = u$, then $x^2 + x + 1 = u^2 + u + 1$.

4. The relation $\{\langle x^2,x \rangle | x \in R\}$ is not a function, because both $\langle 1,1 \rangle$ and $\langle 1,-1 \rangle$ are members.

Synonyms for the word "function" are numerous and include **transformation, map** or **mapping, correspondence,** and **operator.**

If f is a function and $\langle x,y \rangle \in f$, so that xfy, then x is an **argument** of f. There is a great variety of terminology for y; for example, the **value** of f at x, the **image** of x under f, the element into which f **carries** x. There are also various symbols for y: xf, $f(x)$ (or, more simply, fx), x^f. The notation $f(x)$ may be regarded as an abbreviation for $f[\{x\}]$, the set of f-relatives of x. In these terms the characteristic feature of a function among relations in general is that each member of the domain of a function has a single relative.

The student must accustom himself to these various notations, since he will find that all are used. In this book definitions and theorems pertaining to functions will consistently be phrased using the notation $f(x)$, or fx, for the (unique) correspondent of x in a function f. The notation $f[A]$ for $\{y|$ for some x in A, $\langle x,y \rangle \in f\}$ is in harmony with this. However, in applications of functions we shall use a variety of notations. When it is more convenient to use xf in place of $f(x)$, then $[A]f$ will be used in place of $f[A]$. If x^f is used in place of $f(x)$, then $[A]^f$ or A^f will be used in place of $f[A]$.

Since functions are sets, the definition of equality of functions is at hand: Two functions f and g are equal iff they have the same members. It is clear that this may be rephrased $f = g$ iff $D_f = D_g$ and $f(x) = g(x)$ for each x in the common domain. Consequently, a function may be defined by specifying its domain and the value of the function at each member of its domain. The second part of this type of definition is, then, in the nature of a rule. For example, an alternative definition of the function $\{\langle x, x^2 + x + 1 \rangle | x \in \underline{R}\}$ is the function f with $\underline{R}$ as domain and such that $f(x) = x^2 + x + 1$. When a function is defined by specifying its domain and its value at each member of the domain, the range of the function may not be evident. The above example requires a computation to conclude that $R_f = \{x \in \underline{R}|x \geq \frac{3}{4}\}$. On the other hand, it is almost obvious that $R_f \subseteq \underline{R}^+$. In general, one can anticipate difficulty in determining the range, but no difficulty in determining some set that includes the range. Thus, it is convenient to have available the following terminology. A function f is **into** Y iff the range of f is a subset of Y, and f is **onto** Y iff $R_f = Y$. For corresponding notation for the domain of a function we shall say that f is **on** X when the domain of f is X. The symbols

$$f \colon X \to Y \text{ and } X \xrightarrow{f} Y$$

are commonly used to signify that f is a function on the set X into the set Y.

The set of all functions on X into Y is a subset of $\mathcal{P}(X \times Y)$, which we shall symbolize by Y^X. If X is empty, then Y^X consists of only one member, namely, the empty subset of $X \times Y$. This is the only subset of $X \times Y$, since when X is empty so is $X \times Y$. If Y is empty and X is nonempty, then Y^X is empty.

If $f: X \to Y$, and if $A \subseteq X$, then $f \cap (A \times Y)$ is a function on A into Y (called the **restriction** of f to A and abbreviated $f|A$). Explicitly, $f|A$ is the function on A such that $(f|A)(a) = f(a)$ for a in A. A function g is the restriction of a function f to some subset of the domain of f iff the domain of g is a subset of the domain of f and $g(x) = f(x)$ for $x \in D_g$; in other words, $g \subseteq f$. Complementary to the definition of a restriction, the function f is an **extension** of a function g iff $g \subseteq f$. In order to present an example of the notion of a restriction of a function we recall the earlier definition of the identity relation ι_X in X. Clearly, this relation is a function, and hence, in keeping with our current designation of function by lower case English letters, we shall designate it by i or i_X. We shall call i_X the **identity map** on X. If $A \subseteq X$, then $i_X|A = i_A$. If $i_X|A$ is considered as a function on A into X, then it is the **injection mapping** on A into X.

A function is called **one-to-one** if it maps distinct elements onto distinct elements. That is, a function f is one-to-one iff

$$x_1 \neq x_2 \text{ implies } f(x_1) \neq f(x_2).$$

In demonstrating one-to-oneness it may prove to be more convenient to use the contrapositive of the foregoing:

$$f(x_1) = f(x_2) \text{ implies } x_1 = x_2.$$

For example, the function f on $\mathbf{R}$ such that $f(x) = 2x + 1$ is one-to-one since $2x_1 + 1 = 2x_2 + 1$ implies $x_1 = x_2$.

If f is a one-to-one function on X onto Y or, somewhat less awkwardly, if $f: X \to Y$ is one-to-one and onto, then it effects a pairing of the elements of X with those of Y upon matching $f(x)$ in Y with x in X. Indeed, since f is a function, $f(x)$ is a uniquely determined element of Y; since f is onto Y, each y in Y is matched with some x; and since f is one-to-one, each y is matched with only one x. Because of the symmetrical situation that a one-to-one map on X onto Y portrays, it is often called a **one-to-one correspondence between** X **and** Y. Also, two sets so related by some function are said to be in one-to-one correspondence.

EXAMPLES B

1. The familiar exponential function is a function on $\mathbb{R}$ into $\mathbb{R}$, symbolized

$$f: \mathbb{R} \to \mathbb{R} \text{ with } f(x) = e^x.$$

We can also say, more precisely, that f is a function on $\mathbb{R}$ onto $\mathbb{R}^+$. In general, if $f: X \to Y$, then f is a function on X onto $f[X]$, that is, onto the range of f.

2. $\{a,b,c\}^{\{1,2\}}$ is the set of all functions on $\{1,2\}$ into $\{a,b,c\}$. One member of this set is $\{\langle 1,a\rangle, \langle 2,c\rangle\}$.

3. If A and B are sets having the same number of elements, they clearly are in one-to-one correspondence. Then it is an easy matter to show that for any set X, A^X and B^X are in one-to-one correspondence. This being the case, it is customary to denote the set of all functions on X into any set of n elements by n^X. Thus, 2^X denotes the set of all functions on X into a set of two elements, which we will ordinarily take to be $\{0,1\}$. If $A \subseteq X$, then one member of 2^X is the function χ_A defined as follows:

$$\chi_A(x) = 1 \text{ if } x \in A, \text{ and } \chi_A(x) = 0 \text{ if } x \in X - A.$$

We call χ_A the **characteristic function** of A. Now let us define a function f on $\mathcal{P}(X)$ into 2^X by taking as the image of a subset A of X [that is, a member of $\mathcal{P}(X)$] the characteristic function of A (which is a member of 2^X). It is left as an exericse to prove that f is a one-to-one correspondence between $\mathcal{P}(X)$ and 2^X. It is customary to regard $\mathcal{P}(X)$ and 2^X as identified by virtue of this one-to-one correspondence, that is, to feel free to replace one set by the other when it is convenient.

4. If f is a function and A and B are sets, then it can be proved that $f[A \cup B] = f[A] \cup f[B]$ and that $f[A \cap B] \subseteq f[A] \cap f[B]$. The inclusion relation in the case of $A \cap B$ cannot be strengthened.

In elementary mathematics one has occasion to use functions of several variables. Within the framework of our discussion a function of n variables ($n \geq 2$) is simply a function whose arguments are ordered *n*-tuples. We can include the case $n = 1$ if we agree that a 1-tuple, $\langle x \rangle$, is simply x. Introducing the notation X^n for the set of all *n*-tuples $\langle x_1, x_2, \cdots, x_n \rangle$, where each x is a member of the set X, a function, whose domain is X^n and whose range is included in X, is an *n*-**ary operation in** X. In place of "1-ary" we shall say "unary"; for example, complementation is a unary operation in a power set. In place of "2-ary" we shall say "binary." This was anticipated in our discussion of operations for sets; for example, intersection is a binary operation in a suitable collection of sets. Also, addition in $\underline{Z}$ is a binary operation; if $x, y \in \underline{Z}$, the value of this function at $\langle x,y \rangle$ is written $x + y$.

EXERCISES

1. Give an example of a function on $\underline{R}$ onto $\underline{Z}$.
2. Show that if $A \subseteq X$, then $i_X | A = i_A$.
3. If X and Y are sets of n and m element, respectively, Y^X has how many elements? How many members of $\mathcal{P}(X \times Y)$ are functions?
4. Using only mappings of the form $f: \underline{Z}^+ \to \underline{Z}^+$, give an example of a function which
    (a) is one-to-one but not onto;
    (b) is onto but not one-to-one.
5. Let $A = \{1, 2, \cdots, n\}$. Prove that if a map $f: A \to A$ is onto, then it is one-to-one, and that if a map $g: A \to A$ is one-to-one, then it is onto.
6. Let $f: \underline{R}^+ \to \underline{R}$, where $f(x) = \int_1^x \dfrac{dt}{t}$. Show as best you can that f is a one-to-one and onto function.
7. Prove that the function f defined in the third of Examples B is a one-to-one correspondence between $\mathcal{P}(X)$ and 2^X.
8. Referring to the fourth of Examples B, prove that if f is a function and A and B are sets, then $f[A \cup B] = f[A] \cup f[B]$.
9. Referring to the preceding exercise, prove further that $f[A \cap B] \subseteq f[A] \cap f[B]$, and show that proper inclusion can occur.
10. Prove that $f[A \cap B] = f[A] \cap f[B]$ iff f is one-to-one.

Note: In Exercises 11–13 decide which parts can be proved easily, and prove them. Prove the remaining parts after studying Section 1.9.

11. Let A, B, A', and B' be sets such that A and A' are in one-to-one correspondence and B and B' are in one-to-one correspondence. Show that

  (a) there exists a one-to-one correspondence between $A \times B$ and
      $A' \times B'$;
  (b) there exists a one-to-one correspondence between A^B and $A'^{B'}$;
  (c) if, further, $A \cap B = \varnothing$ and $A' \cap B' = \varnothing$, then there exists a
      one-to-one correspondence between $A \cup B$ and $A' \cup B'$.

12. For sets A, B, and C show that
  (a) $A \times B$ is in one-to-one correspondence with $B \times A$;
  (b) $(A \times B) \times C$ is in one-to-one correspondence with
      $A \times (B \times C)$;
  (c) $A \times (B \cup C)$ is in one-to-one correspondence with $(A \times B)$
      $\cup (A \times C)$.

13. For sets A, B, and C show that
  (a) $(A \times B)^C$ is in one-to-one correspondence with $A^C \times B^C$;
  (b) $(A^B)^C$ is in one-to-one correspondence with $A^{B \times C}$;
  (c) if, further, $B \cap C = \varnothing$, then $A^{B \cup C}$ is in one-to-one corres-
      pondence with $A^B \times A^C$.

1.9. Composition and Inversion for Functions

To motivate our next definition, we consider an example. Let the
functions f and g be defined as follows:

$$f: \mathbb{R} \to \mathbb{R} \text{ with } f(x) = 2x + 1,$$
$$g: \mathbb{R}^+ \to \mathbb{R}^+ \text{ with } g(x) = x^{1/2}.$$

It is a familiar experience to derive from such a pair of functions a
function h for which $h(x) = g(f(x))$. Since the domain of g is $\mathbb{R}^+$ by
definition, x must be restricted to real numbers such that $2x + 1 > 0$
for $h(x)$ to be defined. That is, combining f and g in this way yields a
function whose domain is the set of real numbers greater than $-\frac{1}{2}$ and
whose value at x is $g(f(x)) = (2x + 1)^{1/2}$.

The basic idea of this example is incorporated in the following definition. By using ordered pair notation (instead of the domain and
value notation) for functions we avoid having to make any restriction
stemming from a difference between the range of f and the domain of
g. The **composite** of functions f and g, symbolized $g \circ f$, is

$$\{\langle x,z \rangle | \text{ there is a } y \text{ such that } xfy \text{ and } ygz\}.$$

It is left to the reader to prove that this relation is a function. This operation for functions is called (functional) **composition.** The following special case of our definition is worthy of note. If $f: X \to Y$ and $g: Y \to Z$, then $g \circ f: X \to Z$ and $(g \circ f)(x) = g(f(x))$.

The above example establishes the fact that functional composition is not a commutative operation; indeed, rarely does $f \circ g = g \circ f$. However, composition is an associative operation. That is, if f, g, and h are functions, then

$$f \circ (g \circ h) = (f \circ g) \circ h.$$

To prove this, assume that $\langle x,u \rangle \in f \circ (g \circ h)$. Then there exists a z such that $\langle x,z \rangle \in g \circ h$ and $\langle z,u \rangle \in f$. Since $\langle x,z \rangle \in g \circ h$, there exists a y such that $\langle x,y \rangle \in h$ and $\langle y,z \rangle \in g$. Now $\langle y,z \rangle \in g$ and $\langle z,u \rangle \in f$ imply that $\langle y,u \rangle \in f \circ g$. Further, $\langle x,y \rangle \in h$ and $\langle y,u \rangle \in f \circ g$ imply that $\langle x,u \rangle \in (f \circ g) \circ h$. Reversing the foregoing steps yields the reverse inclusion and hence equality.

The foregoing proof will be less opaque to the reader if he rewrites it in terms of function values. The proof given is in accordance with our definition of functional composition and has the merit that it avoids any complications arising from a difference between the range of f and the domain of g. From the associative law for composition follows the general associative law which the reader may formulate. The unique function which is defined by composition from the functions $f_1, f_2, \cdots, f_n$ in that order will be designated by

$$f_1 \circ f_1 \circ \cdots \circ f_n.$$

EXAMPLES A

1. Let $h: \underline{R} \to \underline{R}^+$ where $h(x) = (1 + x^2)^{1/2}$. Then $h = g \circ f$ if $f: \underline{R} \to \underline{R}^+$ with $f(x) = 1 + x^2$, and $g: \underline{R}^+ \to \underline{R}^+$ with $g(x) = x^{1/2}$. It is this decomposition of h which is used in computing its derivative.

2. A decomposition of an arbitrary function along somewhat different lines than that suggested by the preceding example can be given in terms of concepts we have discussed. First we make a definition. If ρ is an equivalence relation with domain X, then

$$j: X \to X/\rho \text{ with } j(x) = [x]$$

is onto the quotient set X/ρ; j is the **canonical** or **natural mapping** on X onto X/ρ. Now, if f is a mapping on X into Y, the relation defined by

$$x_1 \rho x_2 \text{ iff } f(x_1) = f(x_2)$$

is clearly an equivalence relation on X. Let j be the canonical map on X onto X/ρ. We contend that a function g on X/ρ into $f[X]$, the range of f, is defined by setting $g[x] = f(x)$. To prove that g is a function, it must be shown that if $[x] = [y]$ then $f(x) = f(y)$. But $[x] = [y]$ iff $x\rho y$ iff $f(x) = f(y)$; so g is a function. Finally, we let i be the injection of $f[X]$ into Y. Collectively, we have defined three functions j, g, i where

$$j\colon X \to X/\rho \text{ with } j(x) = [x];$$

$$g\colon X/\rho \to f[X] \text{ with } g[x] = f(x);$$

$$i\colon f[X] \to Y \text{ with } i(y) = y.$$

Clearly, j is onto and i is one-to-one. It is left as an exercise to show that g is one-to-one and onto and that

$$f = i \circ g \circ j.$$

This equation is the whole point of the discussion. It proves to be a useful decomposition for an arbitrary function f.

3. If f is a known function with domain X and with range a subset of Y, then the notation $f\colon X \to Y$ for f includes superfluous information. However, it does suggest the consideration of f as a function that is associated with the pair $\langle X,Y \rangle$ of sets X and Y. If $g\colon Y \to Z$ is likewise associated with $\langle Y,Z \rangle$, then we associate the composite function $g \circ f$ with $\langle X,Z \rangle$. The association of each function f with a pair of sets X and Y, such that X is the domain of f and Y includes the range of f and the agreement that the composite $g \circ f$ of $f\colon X \to Y$ and $g\colon W \to Z$ may be formed only if $W = Y$, has certain merits. For example, within this framework it is possible to characterize "onto" (along with "one-to-one") as a property of functions. Further, it sets these forth as dual properties in a sense that will be explained later.

The characterization of one-to-oneness that we can demonstrate is as follows.

(I) Let $f\colon X \to Y$. Then f is one-to-one iff for all functions g and h such that $g\colon Z \to X$ and $h\colon Z \to X$, $f \circ g = f \circ h$ implies $g = h$. Indeed, suppose that f is one-to-one, $g\colon Z \to X$, $h\colon Z \to X$, and that $f \circ g = f \circ h$. Then $f(g(z)) = f(h(z))$ for all z in Z. With f one-to-one it follows that $g(z) = h(z)$ for all z in Z. Hence $g = h$. The proof of the converse is left as an exercise.

A characterization of a function being onto can now be given by a simple alteration of (I).

(II) Let $f: X \to Y$. Then f is onto Y iff for all functions g and h such that $g: Y \to Z$ and $h: Y \to Z$, $g \circ f = h \circ f$ implies $g = h$. The proof is left as an exercise.

With the above characterizations at our disposal the decomposition obtained in Example 2 can be described more neatly as follows. For any function f there exists a function i which is one-to-one, a function j which is onto, and a function g which is one-to-one and onto, such that $f = i \circ g \circ j$.

If the coordinates of each member of a function f (considered as a set of ordered pairs) are interchanged, the result is a relation g which may not be a function. Indeed, g is a function iff $\langle y,x \rangle$ and $\langle y,z \rangle$ in g imply that $x = z$. In terms of f this means that if $\langle x,y \rangle$ and $\langle z,y \rangle$ are in f, then $x = z$, that is, f is one-to-one. If f is one-to-one, the function resulting from f by interchanging the coordinates of members of f is called the **inverse function** of f, symbolized f^{-1}. This operation, which is defined only for one-to-one functions, is called (functional) **inversion.** If f^{-1} exists, then its domain is the range of f, its range is the domain of f, and $x = f^{-1}(y)$ iff $y = f(x)$. Further, f^{-1} is one-to-one and its inverse, $(f^{-1})^{-1}$, is equal to f. If f is a one-to-one function on X onto Y, then f^{-1} is a one-to-one function on Y onto X. Moreover,

$$f^{-1} \circ f = i_X, \text{ and } f \circ f^{-1} = i_Y.$$

There is another important connection between composition and inversion of functions. If f and g are both one-to-one functions, then $g \circ f$ is one-to-one, and

$$(g \circ f)^{-1} = f^{-1} \circ g^{-1}.$$

The proof is left as an exercise.

EXAMPLES B

1. The function $f: \mathbb{R} \to \mathbb{R}$ such that $f(x) = 2x + 1$ is one-to-one. The inverse of f may be written $\{\langle 2x + 1, x \rangle | x \in \mathbb{R}\}$. This is not very satisfying to one who prefers to have a function defined in terms of its domain and its value at each member of the domain. To satisfy this preference, we note that

$$\{\langle 2x + 1, x \rangle | x \in \mathbb{R}\} = \{\langle t, \tfrac{1}{2}(t - 1) \rangle | t \in \mathbb{R}\}.$$

Thus f^{-1} is the function on $\mathbb{R}$ into $\mathbb{R}$ such that $f^{-1}(x) = \tfrac{1}{2}(x - 1)$.

2. The function $g: \underline{R}^+ \to \underline{R}^+$ such that $g(x) = x^2$ is one-to-one, since $x_1^2 = x_2^2$, and both x_1 and x_2 positive imply that $x_1 = x_2$. Then

$$g^{-1}: \underline{R}^+ \to \underline{R}^+ \text{ where } g^{-1}(x) = x^{1/2}.$$

3. The function
$$f: \underline{R} \to \underline{R}^+ \text{ where } f(x) = 10^x$$

is known to be one-to-one and onto. The inverse function is called the **logarithm function** to the base 10, and its value at x is written $\log_{10} x$. The equations

$$\log_{10} 10^x = x, \text{ for } x \in \underline{R}, \text{ and } 10^{\log_{10} x} = x, \text{ for } x > 0,$$

are instances of equations $(f^{-1} \circ f)(x) = x$, for $x \in D_f$, and $(f \circ f^{-1})(x) = x$, for $x \in R_f$, which are true for any one-to-one function.

4. If the inverse of a function f in $\underline{R}$ exists, then the graph of f^{-1} may be obtained from that of f by reflection in the line $y = x$. The proof is left as an exercise.

5. From the fourth of Examples B is Section 1.8, if the inverse of a function f is defined, then $f^{-1}[A \cup B] = f^{-1}[A] \cup f^{-1}[B]$ and $f^{-1}[A \cap B] \subseteq f^{-1}[A] \cap f^{-1}[B]$. The latter identity can be sharpened to $f^{-1}[A \cap B] = f^{-1}[A] \cap f^{-1}[B]$ for inverse functions. The proof is left as an exercise. A set of the form $f^{-1}[A]$ we call the **inverse** or **counter image** of A under f.

EXERCISES

1. Let $f: \underline{R} \to \underline{R}$ where $f(x) = (1 + (1 - x)^{1/3})^{1/5}$. Express f as the composite of four functions, none of which is the identity function.

2. If $f: X \to Y$ and $A \subseteq X$, show that $f|A = f \circ i_A$.

3. Complete the proof of the assertions made in the second of Examples A.

4. Complete the proof of (I) and supply a proof of (II) in the third of Examples A.

5. Prove that $f: A \to B$ is a one-to-one correspondence between A and B iff there exists a map $g: B \to A$ such that $g \circ f = i_A$ and $f \circ g = i_B$.

6. If $f: A \to B$ and $g: B \to C$ are both one-to-one and onto, show that $g \circ f: A \to C$ is one-to-one and onto and that $(g \circ f)^{-1} = f^{-1} \circ g^{-1}$.

7. For a function $f: A \to A$, f^n is the standard abbreviation for

$f \circ f \circ \cdots \circ f$ with n occurrences of f. Suppose $f^n = i_A$. Show that f is one-to-one and onto.

8. Justify the following restatement of Theorem 1.5. Let X be a set. Then there exists a one-to-one correspondence between the equivalence relations on X and the partitions of X.

9. Prove that if the inverse of the function f in $\mathbb{R}$ exists, then the graph of f^{-1} may be obtained from that of f by a reflection in the line $y = x$.

10. Show that each of the following functions has an inverse. Determine the domain of each inverse and its value at each member of its domain. Further, sketch the graph of each inverse.

(a) $f: \mathbb{R} \to \mathbb{R}$ where $f(x) = 2x - 1$.

(b) $f: \mathbb{R} \to \mathbb{R}$ where $f(x) = x^3$.

(c) $f = \{\langle x, (1 - x^2)^{1/2}\rangle | 0 \le x \le 1\}$.

(d) $f = \left\{\langle x, \dfrac{x}{x - 1} \rangle | -2 \le x < 1\right\}$.

11. Establish the identity $(g \circ f)^{-1} = f^{-1} \circ g^{-1}$ for one-to-one functions f and g.

12. Prove that if the inverse of f exists, then $f^{-1}[A \cap B] = f^{-1}[A] \cap f^{-1}[B]$.

1.10. Ordering Relations

In this section we define several types of relations which have their origin in the intuitive notion of an ordering relation (order of precedence), that is, a relation ρ such that for an appropriate set X there are various distinct members x and y of X such that $x\rho y$, but it is not the case that $y\rho x$. Then, by means of ρ, we could decide to put the x and y in question in the order x,y rather than y,x because $x\rho y$, and it is not the case that $y\rho x$. For a set of real numbers the familiar relations $<$, $\le$, and $>$ are used in this capacity. For a collection of sets the relations $\subset$ and $\subseteq$ serve similarly.

The first ordering relation we shall consider has as its defining properties the basic features common to the above relations of $\le$ for numbers and $\subseteq$ for sets. As a preliminary, we define a relation ρ in X as **antisymmetric** iff for each x and y in X the validity of $x\rho y$ and $y\rho x$ imply that $x = y$. A **partial ordering** in a set X is a reflexive, antisymmetric, and transitive relation in X. Since one may wish to consider a partial ordering in X relative to some set other than X (for example, the familiar ordering in $\underline{Z}$ relative to the set of even integers), it is convenient to make the further definition that a relation ρ **partially orders** a set Y iff $\rho \cap (Y \times Y)$ is a partial ordering in Y. The relation $\rho \cap (Y \times Y)$ is the "restriction" of ρ to Y in the sense that it is reduced by all ordered pairs either of whose coordinates are not members of Y.

EXAMPLES A

1. The relation "is an integral multiple of" in $\underline{Z}^+$ is a partial ordering.

2. A hierarchy or a table of organization in a business firm is determined by a partial ordering in some set of positions.

3. If ρ is a partial ordering in X, then $\rho \cap (A \times A)$ partially orders the subset A of X.

4. If ρ is a relation, the **converse** of ρ, symbolized by $\breve{\rho}$, is the relation such that $y\breve{\rho}x$ iff $x\rho y$. If ρ is a partial ordering, then so is its converse.

5. A relation ρ that is reflexive and transitive is a **preordering**. A potential shortcoming of such a relation, in connection with establishing an order of precedence in a set X, is the possibility of ρ being "indifferent" to some distinct pair x,y of objects in the sense that both $x\rho y$ and $y\rho x$. For example, in some population let w be the weight function and h be the height function of individuals so that $w(x)$ and $h(x)$ are the weight and height, respectively, of the individual named x. Then the relation ρ such that $x\rho y$ iff $w(x) \leq w(y)$ and $h(x) \leq h(y)$ is a preordering, but is not a partial ordering if there are two individuals having the same weight and height.

If ρ is a preordering in X, then it determines a partial ordering in a partition of X, according to Exercise 10 of Section 1.7. There it is asserted first that the relation $\sim$ such that $x \sim y$ iff $x\rho y$ and $y\rho x$ is an equivalence relation. Secondly, it is stated that the relation ρ' such that $[x] \rho' [y]$ iff $x\rho y$ is a partial ordering having the accompanying set of equivalent classes $[x]$ as domain. In summary, if ρ is a preordering in X, then it is a partial ordering in the set obtained from X by identifying elements to which it is indifferent.

The foregoing is nicely illustrated by taking ρ as the relation in the set of complex numbers such that $z\rho w$ iff the real part of z is less than, or equal to, the real part of w.

We shall follow custom and designate partial orderings by the symbol $\leq$. If the relation $\leq$ partially orders X, and x and y are members of X, it may or may not be the case that $x \leq y$. If it is not, we write $x \nleq y$. Also, we abbreviate $x \leq y$ and $x \neq y$ to $x < y$ and say x is **less than** y, or x **precedes** y, or y is **greater than** x. We shall also use $y \geq x$ and $y > x$ as alternatives for $x \leq y$ and $x < y$, respectively, when it is convenient.

Defining a relation ρ in X as **irreflexive** iff for no x in X is $x\rho x$, we may assert that if $\leq$ is a partial ordering in X, then $<$ is irreflexive and transitive in X. Conversely, starting with an irreflexive and transitive relation $<$ in X, the relation $\leq$ such that $x \leq y$ iff $x < y$ or $x = y$ is a partial ordering in X. The proofs are left as an exercise. The derivation of $<$ from $\leq$, and vice versa, can be illustrated in concrete terms by the definition of proper inclusion for sets in terms of inclusion, and vice versa. If $\leq$ partially orders the finite set X, the relation $<$ can be expressed in terms of the following concept. An element y of X is a **cover** of x in X iff $x < y$ and there exists no u in X such that $x < u < y$. If $x < y$, then, clearly, elements $x_1, x_2, \cdots, x_n$ of X can be found such that $x = x_1 < x_2 < \cdots < x_n = y$, and each x_{i+1} covers x_i. Conversely, the existence of such a sequence implies that $x < y$.

A relation ρ is a **simple** (or **linear**) **ordering** iff it is a partial ordering such that $x\rho y$ or $y\rho x$ whenever x and y are distinct members of the domain (which is equal to the range) of ρ. A relation ρ **simply orders** a set Y iff $\rho \cap (Y \times Y)$ is a simple ordering in Y. The familiar ordering of the real numbers is a typical example of a simple ordering. In contrast, inclusion for sets is not, in general, a simple ordering.

To point out the obvious, the applications of ordering relations are concerned with the determinations of orderings in various sets. In practice, ordering relations for a given set X are usually generated by assigned or proven structural features of X. That is, certain features of X, such as the existence of a particular type of operation or mapping property, will permit the definition of an ordering relation for X; an example of this nature appears in the exercises for this section. Properties of this ordering relation may then prove useful in deducing and describing further features of X. Therefore, it is convenient to have available terminology which gives primary exphasis to the set rather than to an ordering relation for it.

A **partially ordered set** is an ordered pair $\langle X, \leq \rangle$ such that $\leq$

partially orders X. A **simply ordered set** or **chain** is an ordered pair $\langle X, \leq \rangle$ such that $\leq$ simply orders X. For example, if $\mathfrak{F}$ is a collection of sets, then $\langle \mathfrak{F}, \subseteq \rangle$ is a partially ordered set. Again, if $\leq$ is the usual ordering for the integers, then $\langle \underline{Z}, \leq \rangle$ is a chain. From the standpoint of set theory, it is more economical to treat ordering relations than ordered sets, that is, sets with accompanying order relations. For example, if $\langle X, \leq \rangle$ is a partially ordered set, then $\leq \cap (X \times X)$ is a partial ordering relation in X. Thus, instead of dealing with X and a relation $\leq$ which partially orders it we can deal exclusively with the ordering relation $\leq \cap (X \times X)$, since it determines X as its domain. That is, all statements about ordered sets are equivalent to statements about their ordering relations, and vice versa.

As an illustration of the preceding remark we restate our earlier characterization of $<$ for a finite set X partially ordered by a relation $\leq$. If $\langle X, \leq \rangle$ is a finite partially ordered set, then $x < y$ iff there exists a chain of the form $x = x_1 < x_2 < \cdots < x_n = y$ in which each x_{i+1} covers x_i. This result enables one to represent any finite partially ordered set by a diagram. The elements of X are represented by dots arranged in accordance with the following rule. The dot for x_2 is placed above that for x_1 iff $x_1 < x_2$, and, if x_2 is a cover of x_1, the dots are joined by a line segment. Thus, $x < y$ iff there exists an ascending broken line connecting x with y. Some examples of such diagrams are shown below.

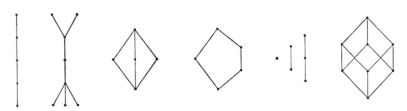

The first is the diagram of a chain with five members. Clearly, the diagram of any chain has this form. The last one is that of the power set of a set of three elements partially ordered by inclusion: the dot at the lowest level represents the empty subset, the dots at the next level represent the unit subsets, and so on. Such diagrams not only serve to represent given partially ordered sets by displaying the ordering relation, but, conversely, also may be used to define partially ordered sets; the ordering relation is just that indicated by the various broken lines.

In preparation for our next definition in connection with partially ordered sets we discuss an example. The set $\{1,2,3,5,6,10,15,30\}$, whose members are the divisors of 30, is partially ordered by the relation $\leq$ where $x \leq y$ iff x is a multiple of y. It is left as an exercise to show that the diagram of this partially ordered set is identical to that given above for the subsets of a set of three elements partially ordered by inclusion. Although these two partially ordered sets are obviously not equal, they are indistinguishable insofar as their structure as partially ordered sets is concerned. This is the essence of the identity of their respective diagrams. When this type of relationship exists between two partially ordered sets it is certainly worthy of note, since any property of one that is expressible in terms of its ordering relation has an analogue in the other. Thus, we propose to formalize this type of indiscernibility. The identity of the diagrams of the two partially ordered sets mentioned above implies, first, the existence of a pairing of the members of the two sets. This can be formulated as the existence of a one-to-one correspondence, which has the advantage that it does not limit us to finite sets. Next, it is implied that the relationship between a pair of elements in one set, as specified by the ordering relation for that set, is the same as that for the corresponding pair in the other set, relative to its ordering relation. The following definition is basic in the precise formulation of this property. A function $f: X \to X'$ is **order preserving** (**isotone**) relative to an ordering $\leq$ for X and an ordering $\leq'$ for X' iff $x \leq y$ implies $f(x) \leq' f(y)$. Then the likeness with which we are concerned can be described as the existence of a one-to-one correspondence such that it and its inverse are order-preserving. The customary terminology in this connection follows. An **isomorphism** between the partially ordered sets $\langle X, \leq \rangle$ and $\langle X', \leq' \rangle$ is a one-to-one correspondence between X and X' such that both it and its inverse are order-preserving. If such a correspondence exists, then one partially ordered set is an **isomorphic image** of the other, or, more simply, the two partially ordered sets are **isomorphic**. Thus, the likeness which we observed between the collection of subsets of a three-element set and the set of divisors of 30, with their respective partial orderings, may be expressed by saying that they are isomorphic partially ordered sets.

When the concept of a partially ordered set was defined it was stated that a collection of sets partially ordered by inclusion is a typical example. This was rather loose talk, since the word "typical" has so many shades of meaning. One precise (and demanding) meaning that might be given is this: Each partially ordered set is isomorphic to a collection of sets partially ordered by inclusion. This is proved next.

THEOREM 1.7.   A partially ordered set $\langle X, \leq \rangle$ is isomorphic to a collection of sets, indeed, a collection of subsets of X, partially ordered by inclusion.

   Proof. For a in X define S_a to be $\{x \in X | x \leq a\}$. Then the mapping f on X into $\{S_a | a \in X\}$ where $f(a) = S_a$ verifies the assertion. The details are left as an exercise.

This result is often stated as: "Each partially ordered set can be represented by a collection of sets (partially ordered by inclusion)." In effect, the theorem means that the study of partially ordered sets is no more general than that of a collection of sets partially ordered by inclusion. In practice the transfer to such a partially ordered set is usually not carried out, since many individual partially ordered sets would lose much of their intuitive content as a result. Finally, we point out that the theorem does *not* assert that each partially ordered set is isomorphic to a collection consisting of all subsets of some set. Such partially ordered sets, that is, those of the form $\langle \mathcal{P}(A), \subseteq \rangle$, do not typify partially ordered sets in general, since they have special features. For example, each contains an element (namely, $\varnothing$) less than every other element and an element (namely, A) greater than every other element.

We conclude this section with the introduction of further terminology for partially ordered sets that will be employed later. A **least** member of a set X relative to a partial ordering $\leq$ is a y in X such that $y \leq x$ for all x in X. If it exists, such an element is unique, so one should speak of *the* least member of X. A **minimal** member of a set X relative to $\leq$ is a y in X such that for no x in X is $x < y$. A minimal member need not be unique, as the second diagram above illustrates. A **greatest** member of X relative to $\leq$ is a y in X such that $x \leq y$ for all x in X. A greatest element, if it exists, is unique, so one should speak of *the* greatest element of X. A **maximal** member of X relative to $\leq$ is a y in X, such that for no x in X is $x > y$.

A partially ordered set $\langle X, \leq \rangle$ is **well-ordered** iff each nonempty subset has a least member. A familiar example of a well-ordered set is the set of nonnegative integers relative to its natural ordering. Any well-ordered set $\langle X, \leq \rangle$ is a chain, since for two distinct elements x and y of X the set $\{x,y\}$ must have a first element, and hence either $x < y$ or $y < x$.

If $\langle X, \leq \rangle$ is a partially ordered set and $A \subseteq X$, then an element x in X is an **upper bound** for A iff, for all a in A, $a \leq x$. Similarly, an element x in X is a **lower bound** for A iff, for all a in A, $x \leq a$. A set may have many upper bounds. An element x in X is a **least upper bound** or **supremum** for A (symbolized, lub A or sup A) iff x is an upper bound for A and $x \leq y$ for all upper bounds for A. In other words, a supremum is an upper bound which is a lower bound for the set of all upper bounds. An element x in X is a **greatest lower bound** or **infinum** for A (symbolized glb A or inf A) iff x is a lower bound for A and $x \geq y$ for any lower bound y for A. It is immediate that if A has a least upper bound, then it is unique, and that the same is true for a greatest lower bound.

EXERCISES

1. Show that if ρ is a partial ordering relation, then so is $\breve{\rho}$.

2. For the set of real-valued continuous functions with the non-negative reals as domain, define $f = O(g)$ to mean that there exist positive constants M and N such that $f(x) \leq Mg(x)$ for all $x > N$. Show that this is a preordering, and define the associated equivalence relation.

3. If $\leq$ is a partial ordering in X, show that $<$ is an irreflexive and transitive relation in X. Conversely, if $<$ is an irreflexive and transitive relation in X, show that the relation $\leq$ such that $x \leq y$ iff $x < y$ or $x = y$ is a partial ordering in X.

4. For what sets A is $\langle \mathcal{P}(A), \subseteq \rangle$ a simply ordered set?

5. Let $\langle X, \leq \rangle$ and $\langle X', \leq' \rangle$ be partially ordered sets. Show that $X \times X'$ is partially ordered by ρ where $\langle x,x' \rangle \rho \langle y,y' \rangle$ iff $x \leq y$ and $x' \leq' y'$. The partially ordered set $\langle X \times X', \rho \rangle$ is the (cartesian) **product** of the given partially ordered sets.

6. The **dual** of a partially ordered set $\langle X, \rho \rangle$ is the partially ordered set $\langle X, \breve{\rho} \rangle$ (see Exercise 1 above). If $\langle X, \leq \rangle$ is a partially ordered set and $a, b \in X$ with $a \leq b$, then the set of all x in X, such that $a \leq x \leq b$, is called the **closed interval** $[a,b]$. Show that the set of intervals of a

partially ordered set $\langle X, \leq \rangle$, partially ordered by inclusion, is isomorphic to a subset of the product of $\langle X, \leq \rangle$ and its dual.

7. A partially ordered set is **self-dual** if it is isomorphic to its dual. Show that
   (a) there are just two nonisomorphic partially ordered sets of two elements, both of which are self-dual, and
   (b) there are five nonisomorphic partially ordered sets of three elements, three of which are self-dual.

8. Show by an example that if $\langle X, \leq \rangle$ and $\langle X', \leq' \rangle$ are partially ordered sets and $f: X \rightarrow X'$ is a one-to-one correspondence which preserves order, then f^{-1} need not preserve order.

9. Given that f is an isomorphism between the partially ordered sets $\langle X, \leq \rangle$ and $\langle X', \leq' \rangle$, show that $x < y$ iff $f(x) <' f(y)$.

10. Supply details for the proof of Theorem 1.7.

11. Let $\langle X, \leq \rangle$ be a partially ordered set. Show that u is a maximal element iff $y \in X$ and $y \geq u$ imply $y = u$. Show that v is a minimal element iff $y \in X$ and $y \leq v$ imply $y = v$.

12. Let $\mathfrak{F}_n$ be the collection of all subsets of $\mathbf{Z}^+$ which have at most n members for n a fixed positive integer, and let $\mathfrak{F}$ be the collection of all finite subsets of $\mathbf{Z}^+$. Show that, relative to inclusion,
   (a) each element of $\mathfrak{F}_n$ having n members is maximal, and
   (b) $\mathfrak{F}$ has no maximal elements.

13. As the elements of a set X we take all square regions which lie inside a given rectangular region which is itself not a square. Relative to inclusion, what are the maximal elements of X?

14. Show that in a chain the notions of a greatest element and a maximal element coincide, and show the same for a least element and a minimal element.

15. Let $\langle X, \leq \rangle$ be a partially ordered set with the property that each nonempty subset which has an upper bound has a least upper bound. Show that each nonempty subset of X which has a lower bound has a greatest lower bound.

16. Show that if $\langle X, \leq \rangle$ is a well-ordered set, then it has the property assumed for the partially ordered set in the preceding exercise.

17. Let X be a set and ρ an operation in X. (Thus, ρ is a function on $X \times X$ into X; let us denote the value of ρ at $\langle x, y \rangle$ by xy.) Suppose that ρ is commutative, associative, and idempotent [that is, $xy = yx$,

$x(yz) = (xy)z$, and $xx = x$ for all $x,y,z \in X$]. For $x, y \in X$ define $x \leq y$ iff $x = xy$. Show that

    (a) $\leq$ partially orders X,

    (b) if X has a least element 0, then $0x = 0$,

    (c) $xy \leq x,y$ and if $z \leq x,y$ then $xy \geq z$.

18. The relation $\leq$ where $m \leq n$ iff m divides n partially orders $\mathbf{Z}^+$. Show that each pair of integers has a least upper bound and a greatest lower bound relative to this ordering.

19. Show that each subset of $\mathcal{P}(A)$ partially ordered by inclusion has a least upper bound and a greatest lower bound.

Chapter 2

Logic

$\mathbf{A}$s we shall study it, mathematical or symbolic logic has two aspects. On one hand it is logic—it is an analytical theory of the art of reasoning whose goal is to systematize and codify principles of valid reasoning. It has emerged from a study of the use of language in argument and persuasion and is based on the identification and examination of those parts of language which are essential for these purposes. It is formal in the sense that it lacks reference to meaning. Thereby it achieves versatility: it may be used to judge the correctness of a chain of reasoning (in particular, a "mathematical proof") solely on the basis of the form (and not the content) of the sequence of statements which make up the chain. There is a variety of symbolic logics. We shall be concerned solely with that one which encompasses most of the deductions of the sort encountered in mathematics. Within the context of logic itself, this is "classical" symbolic logic.

The other aspect of symbolic logic is interlaced with problems relating to the foundations of mathematics. In brief, it amounts to formulating a mathematical theory as a logical system augmented by further axioms. The idea of regarding a mathematical theory as an "applied" system of logic originated with the German mathematician, G. Frege (1848–1925), who developed a system of logic for use in his study of the foundations of arithmetic. The *Principia Mathematica* (1910–1913) of Whitehead and Russell carried on this work of Frege and demonstrated that mathematics could be "reduced to logic." In the later chapter treating axiomatic theories some indication will be given of this approach to mathematical theories.

2.1. The Statement Calculus. Sentential Connectives

In mathematical discourse and elsewhere one constantly encounters declarative sentences which have been formed by modifying a sentence with the word *not* or by connecting sentences with the words *and, or, if . . . then* (or *implies*), and *if and only if*. These five words or combinations of words are called **sentential connectives.** Our first concern here is the analysis of the structure of a **composite sentence** (that is, a declarative sentence in which one or more connectives appear) in terms of its constituent **prime sentences** (that is, sentences which either contain no connectives or, by choice, are regarded as "indivisible"). We shall look first at the connectives individually.

A sentence which is modified by the word "not" is called the **negation** of the original sentence. For example, "2 is not a prime" is the negation of "2 is a prime," and "It is not the case that 2 is a prime and 6 is a composite number" is the negation of "2 is a prime and 6 is a composite number." It is because the latter sentence is composite that grammatical usage forces one to use the phrase "It is not the case that" instead of simply the word "not."

The word "and" is used to join two sentences to form a composite sentence which is called the **conjunction** of the two sentences. For example, the sentence "The sun is shining, and it is cold outside" is the conjunction of the sentences "The sun is shining" and "It is cold outside." In ordinary language various words, such as "but," are used as approximate synonyms for "and"; however, we shall ignore possible differences in shades of meaning which might accompany the use of one in place of the other.

A sentence formed by connecting two sentences with the word "or" is called the **disjunction** of the two sentences. We shall always assume that "or" is used in the inclusive sense (in legal documents this is often expressed by the barbarism "and/or"). Recall that we interpreted "or" in this way in the definition of the union of two sets.

From two sentences we may construct one of the form "If . . . , then . . ."; this is called a **conditional** sentence. The sentence immediately following "If" is the **antecedent,** and the sentence immediately following "then" is the **consequent.** For example, "If $2 > 3$, then $3 > 4$" is a conditional sentence with "$2 > 3$" as antecedent and "$3 > 4$" as consequent. Several other idioms in English which we shall regard as having the same meaning as "If P, then Q" (where P and Q are sentences) are:

> P implies Q;
> P only if Q;
> P is a sufficient condition for Q;
> Q, provided that P;
> Q if P;
> Q is a necessary condition for P.

The words "if and only if" are used to obtain from two sentences a **biconditional** sentence. We regard the biconditional

$$P \text{ if and only if } Q$$

as having the same meaning as

> If P, then Q, and if Q, then P;
> Q is a necessary and sufficient condition for P.

By introducing letters "P," . . . to stand for prime sentences, a special symbol for each connective, and parentheses, as may be needed for punctuation, the connective structure of a composite sentence can be displayed in an effective manner. Our choice of symbols for the connectives is as follows:

> $\sim$ for "not";
> $\wedge$ for "and";
> $\vee$ for "or";
> $\rightarrow$ for "if . . . , then . . .";
> $\leftrightarrow$ for "if and only if."

Thus, if P and Q are sentences, then

$$\sim\!P, \; P \wedge Q, \; P \vee Q, \; P \rightarrow Q, \; P \leftrightarrow Q$$

are, respectively, the negation of P, the conjunction of P and Q, and so on. Following are some concrete examples of analyzing the connective structure of composite sentences in terms of constituent prime sentences.

EXAMPLES

1. The sentence

$$2 \text{ is a prime, and 6 is a composite number}$$

may be symbolized by

$$P \wedge C,$$

where P is "2 is a prime" and C is "6 is a composite number."

2. The sentence

If either the Pirates or the Cubs lose and the Giants win, then the Dodgers will be out of first place and, moreover, I will lose a bet

is a conditional, so it may be symbolized in the form

$$A \rightarrow C.$$

The antecedent is composed from the three prime sentences P ("The Pirates lose"), C ("The Cubs lose"), and G ("The Giants win"), and the consequent is the conjunction of D ("The Dodgers will be out of first place") and B ("I will lose a bet"). The original sentence may be symbolized in terms of these prime sentences by

$$((P \vee C) \wedge G) \rightarrow (D \wedge B).$$

3. The sentence

If either labor or management is stubborn, then the strike will be settled iff the government obtains an injunction, but troops are not sent into the mills.

is a conditional. The antecedent is the disjunction of L ("Labor is stubborn") and M ("Management is stubborn"). The consequent is a biconditional whose lefthand member is S ("The strike will be settled") and whose righthand member is the conjunction of G ("The government obtains an injunction") and the negation of R ("Troops are sent into the mills"). So, the original sentence may be symbolized by

$$(L \vee M) \rightarrow (S \leftrightarrow (G \wedge (\sim R))).$$

To avoid an excess of parentheses in writing composite sentences in symbolic form, we introduce conventions as in algebra. We agree that $\leftrightarrow$ is the strongest connective (that is, it is to encompass most), and then follows $\rightarrow$. Next in order are $\vee$ and $\wedge$, which are assigned equal strength, and then follows $\sim$, the weakest connective. For example,

$$P \wedge Q \rightarrow R \text{ means } (P \wedge Q) \rightarrow R;$$
$$P \leftrightarrow Q \rightarrow R \text{ means } P \leftrightarrow (Q \rightarrow R);$$
$$P \leftrightarrow Q \wedge R \text{ means } P \leftrightarrow (Q \wedge R);$$
$$\sim P \wedge Q \text{ means } (\sim P) \wedge Q;$$

and the third of the Examples above may now be written as

$$L \vee M \rightarrow (S \leftrightarrow G \wedge \sim R).$$

EXERCISES

1. Translate the following composite sentences into symbolic notation, using letters to stand for the prime components (which here we understand to mean sentences which contain no connectives).

    (a) Either it is raining or someone left the shower on.

    (b) If it is foggy tonight, then either John must stay home or he must take a taxi.

    (c) John will sit, and he or George will wait.

    (d) John will sit and wait, or George will wait.

    (e) I will go either by bus or by taxi.

    (f) Neither the North nor the South won the Civil War.

    (g) If, and only if, irrigation ditches are dug will the crops survive; should the crops not survive, then the farmers will go bankrupt and leave.

    (h) If I am either tired or hungry, then I cannot study.

    (i) If John gets up and goes to school, he will be happy; and if he does not get up, he will not be happy.

2. Let C be "Today is clear," R be "It is raining today," S be "It is snowing today," and Y be "Yesterday was cloudy." Translate into acceptable English the following:

    (a) $C \rightarrow \sim(R \wedge S)$;   (d) $(Y \rightarrow R) \vee C$;

    (b) $Y \leftrightarrow C$;   (e) $C \leftrightarrow (R \wedge \sim S) \vee Y$;

    (c) $Y \wedge (C \vee R)$;   (f) $(C \leftrightarrow R) \wedge (\sim S \vee Y)$.

2.2. The Statement Calculus. Truth Tables

Earlier we agreed that by a statement we would understand a declarative sentence which has the quality that it can be classified as either true or false, but not both. That one of "truth" or "falsity" which is assigned to a statement is its **truth value.** Often we shall abbreviate "truth" to T and "falsity" to F. If P and Q are statements, then, using the everyday meaning of the connectives, each of

$$\sim P, P \wedge Q, P \vee Q, P \rightarrow Q, P \leftrightarrow Q$$

is a statement. Let us elaborate.

On the basis of the usual meaning of "not," if a statement is true, its negation is false, and vice versa. For example, if S is the true statement (has truth value T) "The moon is a satellite of the earth," then $\sim S$ is false (has truth value F).

By convention, the conjunction of two statements is true when, and only when, both of its constituent statements are true. For example, "3 is a prime, and $2 + 2 = 5$" is false because "$2 + 2 = 5$" is a false statement.

Having agreed that the connective "or" would be understood in the inclusive sense, standard usage classifies a disjunction as false when, and only when, both constituent statements are false.

Truth-value assignments of the sort which we are making can be summarized concisely by **truth tables** wherein are displayed the truth-value assignments for all possible assignments of truth values to the constituent statements. Below are truth tables for the types of composite statements we have already discussed, as well as those for conditional and the biconditional statements.

Negation	
P	$\sim P$
T	F
F	T

Conjunction		
P	Q	$P \wedge Q$
T	T	T
T	F	F
F	T	F
F	F	F

Disjunction		
P	Q	$P \vee Q$
T	T	T
T	F	T
F	T	T
F	F	F

Conditional		
P	Q	$P \to Q$
T	T	T
T	F	F
F	T	T
F	F	T

Biconditional		
P	Q	$P \leftrightarrow Q$
T	T	T
T	F	F
F	T	F
F	F	T

The motivation for the truth-value assignments made for the conditional is the fact that, as intuitively understood, $P \to Q$ is true iff Q is deducible from P in some way. So, if P is true and Q is false, we want $P \to Q$ to be false, which accounts for the second line of the table. Next, suppose that Q is true. Then, independently of P and its truth value, it is plausible to assert that $P \to Q$ is true. This reasoning suggests the assignments made in the first and third lines of the table. To justify the fourth line, consider the statement $P \wedge Q \to P$. We expect this to be true regardless of the choice of P and Q. But, if P and Q are both false, then $P \wedge Q$ is false, and we are led to the conclusion that if both antecedent and consequent are false, a conditional is true.

The table for the biconditional is determined by that for conjunction and the conditional, once it is agreed that $P \leftrightarrow Q$ means the same as $(P \to Q) \wedge (Q \to P)$.

These five tables are to be understood as definitions; they are the customary definitions adopted for mathematics. We have made merely a feeble attempt to make them seem plausible on the basis of meaning. It is an immediate consequence of these definitions that if P and Q are statements, then so are each of $\sim P$, $P \wedge Q$, $P \vee Q$, $P \to Q$, and $P \leftrightarrow Q$. It follows immediately that any composite sentence whose prime components are statements is itself a statement. If the truth values of the prime components are known, then the truth value of the composite statement can be determined in a mechanical way.

EXAMPLES

1. Suppose that a composite statement is symbolized by

$$P \vee Q \to (R \leftrightarrow \sim S)$$

and that the truth values of P, Q, R, and S are T, F, F, and T, respectively. Then the value of $P \vee Q$ is T, that of $\sim S$ is F, that of $R \leftrightarrow \sim S$

is T, and, hence, that of the original statement is T, as a conditional having a true antecedent and a true consequent. Such a calculation can be made quickly by writing the truth value of each prime statement underneath it and the truth value of each composite constructed under the connective involved. Thus, for the above we would write out the following, where, for study purposes, we have put successive steps on successive lines.

$$
\begin{array}{ccccc}
P \vee Q & \to & (R & \leftrightarrow & \sim S) \\
\text{T} \quad \text{F} & & \text{F} & & \text{T} \\
\text{T} & & & & \text{F} \\
& & & \text{T} & \\
& \text{T} & & &
\end{array}
$$

2. Consider the following argument.

> If prices are high, then wages are high. Prices are high or there are price controls. Further, if there are price controls, then there is not an inflation. There is an inflation. Therefore, wages are high.

Suppose that we are in agreement with each of the first four statements (the premises). Must we accept the fifth statement (the conclusion)? To answer this, let us first symbolize the argument using letters "P," "W," "C," and "I" in the obvious way. Thus, P is the sentence "Prices are high." Then we may present it as follows:

$$
\begin{array}{c}
P \to W \\
P \vee C \\
C \to \sim I \\
\hline
\dfrac{I}{W}
\end{array}
$$

To assume that we are in agreement with the premises amounts to the assignment of the value T to the statements above the line. The question posed then can be phrased as: If the premises have value T, does the conclusion have value T? The answer is in the affirmative. Indeed, since I and $C \to \sim I$ have value T, the value of C is F according to the truth table for the conditional. Hence, P has value T (since $P \vee C$ is T) and, therefore, W has value T (since $P \to W$ is T).

3. We consider the conjunction

$$(P \vee C) \wedge (C \to \sim I)$$

of two of the statements appearing in the preceding example. In general, the truth value which such a statement will receive is dependent on the assignments made to the prime statements involved. It is realistic to assume that, during periods of changing economic conditions, the appropriate truth value assignments to one or more of P, C, and I will change from T to F or vice versa. Thus the question may arise as to combinations of truth values of P, C, and I for which $(P \lor C) \land (C \to {\sim}I)$ has value T or value F. This can be answered by the examination of a truth table in which there appears the truth value of the composite statement for *every* possible assignment (2^3) of truth values to P, C, and I. This is called the truth table for the given statement, and it appears below. Each line includes an assignment of values to P, C, and I, along with the associated value of $(P \lor C) \land (C \to {\sim}I)$. The latter may be computed as in the first example above. However, short cuts in filling out the complete table will certainly occur to the reader as he proceeds.

P	C	I	$(P \lor C) \land (C \to {\sim}I)$
T	T	T	F
T	T	F	T
T	F	T	T
T	F	F	T
F	T	T	F
F	T	F	T
F	F	T	F
F	F	F	F

4. If P is "2 is a prime" and L is "Logic is fun," there is nothing to prohibit our forming such composite statements as

$$P \lor L, P \to L, {\sim}P \to P \lor L.$$

Since both P and L have truth values (clearly, both are T), these composite statements have truth values which we can specify. One's initial reaction to such nonsense might be that it should be prohibited —that the formation of conjunctions, conditionals, and so on, should be permitted only if the component statements are related in content or subject. However, it requires no lengthy reflection to realize the difficulties involved in characterizing such obscure notions. It is much simpler to take the easy way out, namely, to permit the formation of composite statements from any statements. On the basis of meaning, this amounts to nonsense sometimes, but no harm results. Our concern is with the formulation of principles of valid reasoning. In applications to systematic reasoning, composite statements which amount to gibberish simply will not occur.

EXERCISES

1. Suppose that the statements P, Q, R, and S are assigned the truth values T, F, F, and T, respectively. Find the truth value of each of the following statements.

(a) $(P \vee Q) \vee R$.   (f) $P \vee R \leftrightarrow R \wedge \sim S$.

(b) $P \vee (Q \vee R)$.   (g) $S \leftrightarrow P \rightarrow (\sim P \vee S)$.

(c) $R \rightarrow (S \wedge P)$.   (h) $Q \wedge \sim S \rightarrow (P \leftrightarrow S)$.

(d) $P \rightarrow (R \rightarrow S)$.   (i) $R \wedge S \rightarrow (P \rightarrow \sim Q \vee S)$.

(e) $P \rightarrow (R \vee S)$.   (j) $(P \vee \sim Q) \vee R \rightarrow (S \wedge \sim S)$.

2. Construct the truth table for each of the following statements.

(a) $P \rightarrow (P \rightarrow Q)$.   (d) $(P \rightarrow Q) \leftrightarrow \sim P \vee Q$.

(b) $P \vee Q \leftrightarrow Q \vee P$.   (e) $(P \rightarrow Q \wedge R) \vee (\sim P \wedge Q)$.

(c) $P \rightarrow \sim (Q \wedge R)$.   (f) $P \wedge Q \rightarrow (Q \wedge \sim Q \rightarrow R \wedge Q)$.

3. Suppose the value of $P \rightarrow Q$ is T; what can be said about the value of $\sim P \wedge Q \leftrightarrow P \vee Q$?

4. (a) Suppose the value of $P \leftrightarrow Q$ is T; what can be said about the values of $P \leftrightarrow \sim Q$ and $\sim P \leftrightarrow Q$?

    (b) Suppose the value of $P \leftrightarrow Q$ is F; what can be said about the values of $P \leftrightarrow \sim Q$ and $\sim P \leftrightarrow Q$?

5. For each of the following determine whether the information given is sufficient to decide the truth value of the statement. If the information is enough, state the truth value. If it is insufficient, show that both truth values are possible.

(a) $(P \rightarrow Q) \rightarrow R$.
          T

(b) $P \wedge (Q \rightarrow R)$.
          T

(c) $P \vee (Q \rightarrow R)$.
          T

(d) $\sim (P \vee Q) \leftrightarrow \sim P \wedge \sim Q$.
          T

(e) $(P \rightarrow Q) \rightarrow (\sim Q \rightarrow \sim P)$.
          T

(f) $(P \wedge Q) \rightarrow (P \vee S)$.
       T   F

6. In the third Example in Section 2.1 we symbolized the statement

> If either labor or management is stubborn, then the
> strike will be settled iff the government obtains an in-
> junction, but troops are not sent into the mills

as

$$L \lor M \to (S \leftrightarrow G \land \sim R).$$

By a truth-value analysis, determine whether this statement is true or
false under each of the following assumptions.

   (a) Labor is stubborn, management is not, the strike will be
settled, the government obtains an injunction, and troops
are sent into the mills.

   (b) Both labor and management are stubborn, the strike will not
be settled, the government fails to obtain an injunction, and
troops are sent into the mills.

7. Referring to the statement in the preceding exercise, suppose it
is agreed that

> If the government obtains an injunction, then troops
> will be sent into the mills. If troops are sent into the
> mills, then the strike will not be settled. The strike will
> be settled. Management is stubborn.

Determine whether the statement in question is true or not.

2.3. The Statement Calculus. Validity

The foregoing is intended to suggest the nature of the statement
calculus, namely, the analysis of those logical relations among sentences
which depend solely on their composition from constituent sentences
using sentential connectives. The setting for such an analysis includes
the presence of an initial set of sentences (the "prime sentences") and
the following two assumptions:

(i) Each prime sentence is a statement; that is, there may be assigned
to a prime sentence a truth value.

(ii) Each sentence under consideration is composed from prime
sentences using sentential connectives and, for a given assignment of
truth values to these prime sentences, receives a truth value in accordance with the truth tables given earlier for negation, conjunction, and
so on.

With this in mind let us make a fresh start on the statement calculus. Suppose there is given a nonempty set of distinct sentences and that we extend this set by adjoining precisely all of those sentences which can be formed using, repeatedly, and in all possible ways, the various sentential connectives. Then the extended set has the following property. If A and B are members, then so are each of $\sim A$, $A \vee B$, $A \wedge B$, $A \rightarrow B$, and $A \leftrightarrow B$. We shall call the members of the extended class **formulas.** The members of the initial set are the **prime formulas,** and the others are **composite formulas.** The prime formulas which appear in a composite formula are said to be contained in that formula and are called its prime components. To display a composite formula unambiguously, parentheses are used. However, to avoid excessive use of parentheses, the conventions introduced earlier will be employed.

The classical statement calculus, which is the only one we treat, assumes that with each prime formula there is associated exactly one member of $\{T, F\}$. Further, it assumes that which of T and F is associated with a prime formula is irrelevant. Thereby, maximum versatility in the applications is achieved—truth values may be assigned as the occasion demands. The truth value of a composite formula is defined inductively in accordance with the following tables.

A B	$A \wedge B$	$A \vee B$	$A \rightarrow B$	$A \leftrightarrow B$	A	$\sim A$
T T	T	T	T	T	T	F
T F	F	T	F	F	F	T
F T	F	T	T	F		
F F	F	F	T	T		

EXAMPLES A

1. If the prime components in a formula A are P_1, P_2, $\cdots$, P_n, then the definition of the truth value of A in terms of truth values of P_1, P_2, $\cdots$, P_n can be exhibited in a truth table, as described earlier. There are 2^n rows in such a table, each row exhibiting one possible assignment of T's and F's to P_1, P_2, $\cdots$, P_n.

2. A **truth function** is a function on V^n into V where $V = \{T, F\}$ and $n \geq 1$. That is, a truth function is a function of n arguments where each argument can assume either T or F as a value and each function value is either T or F. We shall designate truth functions by such symbols as

$$f(p_1, p_2, \cdots, p_n), g(q_1, q_2, \cdots, q_n), \text{ and so on.}$$

Note that we depart from our practice of designating functions by single letters and use notation heretofore reserved for function values. Our excuse is that composition of functions can be described more simply. For example, the notation

$$f(p_1, \cdots, p_{i-1}, g(q_1, \cdots, q_m), p_{i+1}, \cdots, p_n)$$

is self-explanatory as a function obtained by composition from the truth function f of n arguments and g of m arguments. We shall refer to this function as that obtained by substitution of g for the ith variable in f. Clearly, such combinations of truth functions are again truth functions.

An alternative approach to the statement calculus can be given in terms of truth functions: There are 2^{2^n} different truth functions of n variables. Of the four for $n = 1$, that one whose value at T is F and whose value at F is T we denote by $\sim p$. Of the sixteen truth functions for $n = 2$, we single out four; definitions of, and notations for, these functions appear in the following table.

	$\wedge(p,q)$	$\vee(p,q)$	$\rightarrow(p,q)$	$\leftrightarrow(p,q)$
$\langle\mathsf{T,T}\rangle$	T	T	T	T
$\langle\mathsf{T,F}\rangle$	F	T	F	F
$\langle\mathsf{F,T}\rangle$	F	T	T	F
$\langle\mathsf{F,F}\rangle$	F	F	T	T

It is obvious that we have simply mimicked the symbols for, and truth tables of, conjunction, disjunction, and so on. The outfix notation for these functions seems unnatural; we shall put the reader at ease by usually employing the familiar infix notation [for example, $p \wedge q$ instead of $\wedge(p,q)$].

Henceforth, let us restrict our usage of the term "truth function" to members of the set $\mathfrak{J}$ defined inductively as follows:

(I) Each of the functions $\sim p$, $p \wedge q$, $p \vee q$, $p \rightarrow q$, and $p \leftrightarrow q$ is a member of $\mathfrak{J}$.

(II) If $f \in \mathfrak{J}$, then so is the function obtained by substitution of f for one of the variables in any one of the functions in (I).

(III) A function is a member of $\mathfrak{J}$ iff it can be accounted for on the basis of (I) and (II).

The following are examples of truth functions:

$$(\sim p) \vee q,$$
$$\sim (p \vee q),$$
$$(\sim p) \to (q \vee (r \wedge s)).$$

Clearly, each truth function, when defined using the notation we have agreed on, determines a formula as defined above, and, conversely, each formula may be considered as a truth function. Further, it should be clear that it is the structure of a composite formula A regarded as a function which one considers in order to make a truth value assignment to A for a given assignment of truth values to its prime components. When it is convenient, we shall feel free to regard a formula as a truth function. In such an event, the prime components (statement letters) will be considered as variables which can assume the values T and F.

The statement calculus is concerned with the truth values of composite formulas in terms of truth-value assignments to the prime components and the interrelations of the truth values of composite formulas having some prime components in common. As we proceed in this study it will appear that those formulas whose truth value is T for every assignment of truth values to its prime components occupy a central position. A formula whose value is T, for all possible assignments of truth values to its prime components, is a **tautology** or, alternatively, such a formula is **valid** (in the statement calculus). We shall often write

$$\models A\dagger$$

for "A is valid" or "A is a tautology." Whether or not a formula A is a tautology can be determined by an examination of its truth table. If the prime components in A are $P_1, P_2, \cdots, P_n$, then A is a tautology iff its value is T for each of the 2^n assignments of T's and F's to $P_1, P_2, \cdots, P_n$. For example, $P \to P$ and $P \wedge (P \to Q) \to Q$ are tautologies, whereas $P \to (Q \to R)$ is not. These conclusions are based on an examination of Tables I, II, and III below.

† This symbol for validity appears to be due to Kleene.

Table I		Table II		Table III	

P	$P \to P$
T	T
F	T

P	Q	$P \wedge (P \to Q) \to Q$		
T	T	T	T	T
T	F	F	F	T
F	T	F	T	T
F	F	F	T	T

P	Q	R	$P \to (Q \to R)$	
T	T	T	T	T
T	T	F	F	F
T	F	T	T	T
T	F	F	T	T
F	T	T	T	T
F	T	F	T	F
F	F	T	T	T
F	F	F	T	T

The definition of validity provides us with a mechanical way to decide whether a given formula is valid, namely, the computation and examination of its truth table. Although it may be tedious, this method can always be used to test a proposed formula for validity. But, clearly, it is an impractical way to discover tautologies. This state of affairs has prompted the derivation of rules for generating tautologies from tautologies. The knowledge of a limited number of simple tautologies and several such rules make possible the derivation of a great variety of valid formulas. We develop next several such rules and then implement them with a list of useful tautologies.

THEOREM 2.1.   Let B be a formula and let B^* be the formula resulting from B by the substitution of a formula A for all occurrences of a prime component P contained in B. If $\models B$, then $\models B^*$.

Proof.   For an assignment of values to the prime components of B^* there results a value $v(A)$ of A and a value $v(B^*)$ of B^*. Now $v(B^*) = v(B)$, the value of B for a particular assignment of values to its prime components, including the assignment of $v(A)$ to P. If B is valid, then $v(B)$ and hence $v(B^*)$ is always T. That is, if B is valid, then so is B^*.

EXAMPLES B

1. From Table IV below it follows that $\models P \vee Q \leftrightarrow Q \vee P$. Hence, by Theorem 2.1, $\models (R \to S) \vee Q \leftrightarrow Q \vee (R \to S)$. A direct verification of this result (Table V) using the reasoning employed in the proof of Theorem 2.1 should clarify matters, if need be. To explain the relationship of Table V to Table IV, we discuss the displayed line of Table V.

Table IV   Table V

P	Q	$P \vee Q \leftrightarrow Q \vee P$
T	T	T
T	F	T
F	T	F T I T I T F
F	F	T

R	S	Q	$(R \rightarrow S) \vee Q \leftrightarrow Q \vee (R \rightarrow S)$
T	F	T	F T T F

There was entered first (at two places) the value F of $R \rightarrow S$ for the assignment of T to R and F to S. Then the value T assigned to Q was entered twice. The rest of the computation is then a repetition of that appearing in the third line of Table IV after the entries underlined there have been made.

2. The formula $(R \vee Q) \wedge (R \vee Q \rightarrow Q) \rightarrow Q$ is a tautology obtained from the tautology $P \wedge (P \rightarrow Q) \rightarrow Q$ (Table II) by a substitution of the type described in Theorem 2.1.

We introduce next a relation for formulas. For the definition it is convenient to interpret formulas as truth functions and observe that a formula whose prime components are $P_1, P_2, \cdots, P_n$ may be regarded as a function of an extended list $P_1, \cdots, P_n, \cdots, P_m$ of variables. Let us now agree to call formula A **equivalent to** formula B, symbolized A eq B, iff they are equal as truth functions of the list of variables $P_1, P_2, \cdots, P_m$ where each P occurs as a prime component in at least one of A and B. In terms of truth tables, the definition amounts to this. Suppose that $\{P_1, P_2, \cdots, P_m\}$ is the union of the sets of prime components contained in A and B, respectively, and that we compute the truth tables of A and of B as if both contained $P_1, P_2, \cdots, P_m$ as prime components. Then A eq B iff the resulting truth tables are the same. For example, from Tables VI and VII below we infer that $(P \rightarrow Q)$ eq $\sim P \vee Q$ and P eq $P \wedge (Q \vee \sim Q)$.

Table VI   Table VII

P	Q	$P \rightarrow Q$	$\sim P \vee Q$
T	T	T	T
T	F	F	F
F	T	T	T
F	F	T	T

P	Q	P	$P \wedge (Q \vee \sim Q)$
T	T	T	T
T	F	T	T
F	T	F	F
F	F	F	F

It is left as an exercise to prove that eq is an equivalence relation on every set of formulas and, further, that it has the following substitutivity property: If C_A is a formula containing a specific occurrence of the formula A and C_B is the result on replacing this occurrence of A by a formula B, then

if B eq A, then C_B eq C_A.

Henceforth, equivalent formulas will be regarded as interchangeable, and the substitution property will often be employed without comment. Equivalence of formulas can be characterized in terms of the concept of a valid formula, according to the following theorem.

THEOREM 2.2. $\models A \leftrightarrow B$ iff A eq B.

Proof. Let P_1, P_2, $\cdots$, P_m be the totality of prime components appearing in A and B. For a given assignment of truth values to these components, the first part of the computation of the value of $A \leftrightarrow B$ consists of computing the values of A and B, after which the computation is concluded by applying the table for the biconditional. According to this table, the value of $A \leftrightarrow B$ is $\top$ iff the values computed for A and B are the same.

COROLLARY.   Let C_A be a formula containing a specified occurrence of the formula A and let C_B be the result of replacing this occurrence of A by a formula B. If $\models A \leftrightarrow B$, then $\models C_A \leftrightarrow C_B$. If $\models A \leftrightarrow B$ and $\models C_A$, then $\models C_B$.

Proof.   This is left as an exercise.

THEOREM 2.3.   If $\models A$ and $\models A \rightarrow B$, then $\models B$.

Proof. Let P_1, P_2, $\cdots$, P_m be the totality of prime components appearing in A and B. For a given assignment of truth values to these, the first part of the computation of the value of $A \rightarrow B$ consists of computing the values of A and B, after which the computation is completed by applying the table for the conditional. The assumptions $\models A$ and $\models A \rightarrow B$ imply that both the value obtained for A and that for $A \rightarrow B$ are $\top$. According to the table for $A \rightarrow B$, this implies that B must also have the value $\top$. Since this is the case for all assignments of values to P_1, P_2, $\cdots$, P_m, B is valid.

As the next theorem we list a collection of tautologies. It is not intended that these be memorized, but rather they should be used for reference. That many of the biconditionals listed are tautologies should be highly plausible on the basis of meaning, together with Theorem 2.1. That each is a tautology may be demonstrated by constructing a truth table for it, regarding the letters present as prime formulas. Then, once it is shown that the value is $\top$ for all assignments of values to the components, an appeal is made to the substitution rule of Theorem 2.1 to remove the restriction that the letters be prime formulas. In the exercises for this section the reader is asked to establish the validity of some of the later formulas by applying one or more of Theorems 2.1–2.3 to tautologies appearing earlier in the list.

THEOREM 2.4.

Tautological Conditionals

1. $\models A \wedge (A \rightarrow B) \rightarrow B$.
2. $\models {\sim}B \wedge (A \rightarrow B) \rightarrow {\sim}A$.
3. $\models {\sim}A \wedge (A \vee B) \rightarrow B$.
4. $\models A \rightarrow (B \rightarrow A \wedge B)$.
5. $\models A \wedge B \rightarrow A$.
6. $\models A \rightarrow A \vee B$.
7. $\models (A \rightarrow B) \wedge (B \rightarrow C) \rightarrow (A \rightarrow C)$.
8. $\models (A \wedge B \rightarrow C) \rightarrow (A \rightarrow (B \rightarrow C))$.
9. $\models (A \rightarrow (B \rightarrow C)) \rightarrow (A \wedge B \rightarrow C)$.
10. $\models (A \rightarrow B \wedge {\sim}B) \rightarrow {\sim}A$.
11. $\models (A \rightarrow B) \rightarrow (A \vee C \rightarrow B \vee C)$.
12. $\models (A \rightarrow B) \rightarrow (A \wedge C \rightarrow B \wedge C)$.
13. $\models (A \rightarrow B) \rightarrow ((B \rightarrow C) \rightarrow (A \rightarrow C))$.
14. $\models (A \leftrightarrow B) \wedge (B \leftrightarrow C) \rightarrow (A \leftrightarrow C)$.

Tautological Biconditionals

15. $\models A \leftrightarrow A$.
16. $\models {\sim}{\sim}A \leftrightarrow A$.
17. $\models (A \leftrightarrow B) \leftrightarrow (B \leftrightarrow A)$.
18. $\models (A \rightarrow B) \wedge (C \rightarrow B) \leftrightarrow (A \vee C \rightarrow B)$.
19. $\models (A \rightarrow B) \wedge (A \rightarrow C) \leftrightarrow (A \rightarrow B \wedge C)$.
20. $\models (A \rightarrow B) \leftrightarrow ({\sim}B \rightarrow {\sim}A)$.
21. $\models A \vee B \leftrightarrow B \vee A$.   21′. $\models A \wedge B \leftrightarrow B \wedge A$.

22. $\models (A \lor B) \lor C \leftrightarrow$
  $A \lor (B \lor C)$.

22'. $\models (A \land B) \land C \leftrightarrow$
  $A \land (B \land C)$.

23. $\models A \lor (B \land C) \leftrightarrow$
  $(A \lor B) \land (A \lor C)$.

23'. $\models A \land (B \lor C) \leftrightarrow$
  $(A \land B) \lor (A \land C)$.

24. $\models A \lor A \leftrightarrow A$.

24'. $\models A \land A \leftrightarrow A$.

25. $\models {\sim}(A \lor B) \leftrightarrow$
  ${\sim}A \land {\sim}B$.

25'. $\models {\sim}(A \land B) \leftrightarrow$
  ${\sim}A \lor {\sim}B$.

Tautologies for Elimination of Connectives

26. $\models A \rightarrow B \leftrightarrow {\sim}A \lor B$.
27. $\models A \rightarrow B \leftrightarrow {\sim}(A \land {\sim}B)$.
28. $\models A \lor B \leftrightarrow {\sim}A \rightarrow B$.
29. $\models A \lor B \leftrightarrow {\sim}({\sim}A \land {\sim}B)$.
30. $\models A \land B \leftrightarrow {\sim}(A \rightarrow {\sim}B)$.
31. $\models A \land B \leftrightarrow {\sim}({\sim}A \lor {\sim}B)$.
32. $\models (A \leftrightarrow B) \leftrightarrow (A \rightarrow B) \land (B \rightarrow A)$.

We conclude this section with the description of a powerful method for obtaining tautologies from scratch. Initially we consider only formulas composed from prime formulas $P_1, P_2, \cdots, P_n$ using ${\sim}$, $\land$, and $\lor$. The **denial**, A_d, of such a formula A is the formula resulting from A by replacing each occurrence of $\land$ by $\lor$ and vice versa and replacing each occurrence of P_i by an occurrence of ${\sim}P_i$ and vice versa. As illustrations of denials in the present context we note that the denial of $P \lor Q$ is ${\sim}P \land {\sim}Q$ and the denial of ${\sim}({\sim}P \land Q)$ is ${\sim}(P \lor {\sim}Q)$. The theorem relating denials and tautologies follows.

THEOREM 2.5.   Let A be a formula composed from prime components using only ${\sim}$, $\land$, and $\lor$. Let A_d be the denial of A. Then $\models {\sim}A \leftrightarrow A_d$.

A proof of this assertion can be given by induction on the number of symbols appearing in a formula. We forego this, but do include in the first example below a derivation of an instance of the theorem. Another example describes the extension of the theorem to the case of a formula which involves $\rightarrow$ or $\leftrightarrow$.

EXAMPLES C

1. An instance of Theorem 2.5 is the assertion that

$$\vDash \sim((\sim P \lor Q) \lor (Q \land (R \lor \sim P))) \leftrightarrow$$
$$(P \land \sim Q) \land (\sim Q \lor (\sim R \land P)),$$

or, in other words, that the lefthand side and the righthand side of the biconditional are equivalent formulas. Using the properties of transitivity and substitutivity of equivalence, this is established below. Each step is justified by the indicated part of Theorem 2.4 (in view of Theorem 2.2).

$$\sim((\sim P \lor Q) \lor (Q \land (R \lor \sim P)))$$

eq $\sim(\sim P \lor Q) \land \sim(Q \land (R \lor \sim P))$	(25)
eq $(\sim\sim P \land \sim Q) \land (\sim Q \lor \sim(R \lor \sim P))$	(25, 25')
eq $(\sim\sim P \land \sim Q) \land (\sim Q \lor (\sim R \land \sim\sim P))$	(25)
eq $(P \land \sim Q) \land (\sim Q \lor (\sim R \land P))$	(16)

2. Using tautology 32 in Theorem 2.4 we can derive from a formula in which $\leftrightarrow$ appears an equivalent formula in which $\leftrightarrow$ is absent. For instance,

$$P \leftrightarrow (Q \land R) \text{ eq } (P \to Q \land R) \land (Q \land R \to P).$$

That is, $\leftrightarrow$ can be eliminated from any formula. Similarly, using tautology 26 or 27, $\to$ can be eliminated from any formula. Thus, any formula A is equivalent to a formula B composed from prime components using $\sim$, $\land$, and $\lor$. Then we may define the denial of A to be the denial of B.

3. According to the preceding example, $\leftrightarrow$ and $\to$ can be eliminated from any formula. Using tautology 29 it is possible to eliminate $\lor$ or (with tautology 31), equally well, $\land$. That is, any formula is equivalent to one composed from prime components using $\sim$ and $\lor$ or using $\sim$ and $\land$.

4. From tautology 22 follows the general associative law for $\lor$ which asserts that however parentheses are inserted in $A_1 \lor A_2 \lor \cdots \lor A_n$ to render it unambiguous, the resulting formulas are equivalent. From tautology 22' follows the corresponding result for $\land$.

EXERCISES

1. Referring to the second of Examples A, write each of the following formulas as a truth function in outfix notation. For example $\sim P \to (Q \vee (R \wedge S))$ becomes $\to (\sim P, \vee (Q, \wedge (R,S)))$.

(a) $P \wedge \sim Q$.
(b) $\sim P \to Q$.
(c) $P \vee (Q \vee R)$.
(d) $P \wedge (Q \to R)$.

(e) $P \to (Q \to R) \leftrightarrow Q \to (P \to R)$.
(f) $P \vee R \to (R \wedge (S \vee \sim P))$.
(g) $(P \to Q) \to (S \wedge \sim P \to Q)$.

2. Suppose that $P_1, P_2, \cdots, P_n$ are the prime components of A. Show that the truth table of A, regarded as having $P_1, \cdots, P_n, \cdots, P_m$ as prime components can be divided into 2^{m-n} parts, each a duplicate of the truth table for A computed with $P_1, P_2, \cdots, P_n$ as the prime components.

3. Prove that eq is an equivalence relation on every set of formulas and that it has the substitutivity property described in the text.

4. Prove the results stated in the Corollary to Theorem 2.2.

5. Derive each of tautologies 28–31 from earlier tautologies in Theorem 2.4, using properties of equivalence for formulas. As an illustration, we derive tautology 27 from earlier ones. From 26, $A \to \sim B$ eq $\sim A \vee \sim B$, and, in turn, $\sim A \vee \sim B$ eq $\sim (A \wedge B)$ by 25'. Hence, $A \to \sim \sim \sim B$ eq $\sim (A \wedge \sim B)$. Using 16 it follows that $A \to B$ eq $\sim (A \wedge \sim B)$, which amounts to 27.

6. Suppose the truth table of a formula containing $P_1, P_2, \cdots, P_n$ as its prime components is given. Describe how to construct a formula A in terms of $\sim$, $\wedge$, and $\vee$, and having $P_1, P_2, \cdots, P_n$ as prime components, which has the given truth table as its truth table. Hint: If, according to the table, the truth value of the formula is F for all assignments to $P_1, P_2, \cdots, P_n$, then for A we may choose $(P_1 \wedge \sim P_1) \wedge (P_2 \wedge \sim P_2) \wedge \cdots \wedge (P_n \wedge \sim P_n)$. If at least one line of the table is T, then form all the 2^n possible combinations of the form $P_1 \wedge P_2 \wedge \cdots \wedge P_n$, $\sim P_1 \wedge P_2 \wedge \cdots \wedge P_n$, $\cdots$, $P_1 \wedge P_2 \wedge \cdots \wedge \sim P_n$, $\cdots$, $\sim P_1 \wedge \sim P_2 \wedge \cdots \wedge \sim P_n$ obtained by negating none, some, or all letters in all possible combinations. Then for A we may choose the disjunction of certain ones of this set.

7. Instead of using truth tables to compute the value of a formula, an arithmetic procedure may be used. The basis for this approach

consists of the following conventions.

  (i) The representation of $\top$ by 0 and F by 1.

  (ii) The interpretation of a formula as a truth function wherein each prime component is a variable which can be assigned the values 0 and 1.

  (iii) The computations of sums and products involving 0 and 1 as in ordinary arithmetic, with one exception, namely, $1 + 1 = 0$.

With the above in mind, the basic truth functions are given by the following formulas.

$$\sim P = 1 + P;$$
$$P \wedge Q = P + Q + PQ;$$
$$P \vee Q = PQ;$$
$$P \rightarrow Q = (1 + P)Q;$$
$$P \leftrightarrow Q = P + Q.$$

We leave it as an exercise to check the foregoing assertion.

  In these terms tautologies are those truth functions which are identically 0. For example, that $\models P \vee \sim P$ is clear from the fact that $P \vee \sim P = P(1 + P)$. To prove that the formula in 1 of Theorem 2.4 (regarding A and B as prime components) is a tautology, we form first [corresponding to $A \wedge (A \rightarrow B)$], $A + (1 + A)B + A(1 + A)B$, which reduces to $A + (1 + A)B$ since $A(1 + A)B$ is identically 0. Then the entire formula in 1 yields the function $(1 + A + (1 + A)B)B$. This gives 0 for $B = 0$, and if $B = 1$, it reduces to $1 + A + (1 + A) = 0$.

  In the algebra at hand, $2x = 0$, $x(x + 1) = 0$, and, for all x, $x^2 = x$. These facts make the simplification of long expressions an easy matter.

  Prove some of the tautologies in Theorem 2.4 by this method.

2.4. The Statement Calculus. Valid Consequence

  In the introduction to this chapter we said that it was a function of logic to provide principles of reasoning, that is, a theory of inference. In practical terms this amounts to supplying criteria for deciding in a mechanical way whether a chain of reasoning will be accepted as correct on the basis of its form. A chain of reasoning is simply a finite sequence of statements which are supplied to support the contention that the last statement in the sequence (the conclusion) may be inferred from certain initial statements (the premises). In everyday circumstances the premises of an inference are judged to be true (on the basis of experience, experiment, or belief). Acceptance of the premises of an inference as true and of the principles employed in a chain of reasoning from such premises as correct commits one to regard the conclusion at hand as true. In a mathematical theory the situation is different. There, one is concerned solely with the conclusions (the so-called "theorems" of the theory) which can be inferred from an assigned initial set of statements (the so-called "axioms" of the theory) according to rules which are specified by some system of logic. In particular, the notion of truth plays no part whatsoever in the theory proper. The contribution of the statement calculus to a theory of inference is just this: It provides a criterion, along with practical working forms thereof, for deciding when the concluding sentence (a statement) of an argument is to be assigned the value $\top$ if each premise of the argument is assigned the truth value $\top$. This criterion is in the form of a definition. The statement B is a **valid consequence** of statements $A_1, A_2, \cdots, A_m$ (by the statement calculus), symbolized

$$A_1, A_2, \cdots, A_m \models B,$$

iff for every truth-value assignment to each of the prime formulas $P_1, P_2, \cdots, P_n$ occurring in one or more of $A_1, A_2, \cdots, A_m$, and B, the formula B receives the value $\top$ whenever every A receives the value $\top$. In terms of truth tables, "$A_1, A_2, \cdots, A_m \models B$" means simply that if truth tables are constructed for $A_1, A_2, \cdots, A_m$, and B, from the list $P_1, P_2, \cdots, P_n$ of prime formulas occurring in one or more of these formulas, then B receives the value $\top$ at least for each assignment to the P's which make all A's simultaneously $\top$.

EXAMPLE A

From an inspection of Table VIII below we obtain the following three illustrations of our definition:

$$P, R, Q \wedge P \rightarrow \sim R \models \sim Q; \qquad \text{(line 3)}$$
$$P, P \rightarrow R, R \models P \vee Q \rightarrow R; \qquad \text{(lines 1 and 3)}$$
$$Q \wedge P \rightarrow \sim R, \sim Q, P \rightarrow R \models \sim(P \wedge Q). \qquad \text{(lines 3, 7, 8)}$$

Table VIII

P	Q	R	$Q \wedge P \rightarrow \sim R$	$\sim Q$	$P \rightarrow R$	$P \vee Q \rightarrow R$	$\sim(P \wedge Q)$
T	T	T	F	F	T	T	F
T	T	F	T	F	F	F	F
T	F	T	T	T	T	T	T
T	F	F	T	T	F	F	T
F	T	T	T	F	T	T	T
F	T	F	T	F	T	F	T
F	F	T	T	T	T	T	T
F	F	F	T	T	T	T	T

THEOREM 2.6.

(I) $A \vDash B$ iff $\vDash A \rightarrow B$.

(II) $A_1, A_2, \cdots, A_m \vDash B$ iff $A_1 \wedge A_2 \wedge \cdots \wedge A_m \vDash B$ or, iff $\vDash A_1 \wedge A_2 \wedge \cdots \wedge A_m \rightarrow B(m \geq 2)$.

Proof. For (I), let $A \vDash B$. By the table for $\rightarrow$, $A \rightarrow B$ receives the value F iff A receives the value T, and, simultaneously, B receives the value F. From the hypothesis, this combination of values does not occur. Hence $A \rightarrow B$ always receives the value T, that is, $\vDash A \rightarrow B$. For the converse, let $\vDash A \rightarrow B$, and consider an assignment of values to the prime components such that A receives the value T. Since $A \rightarrow B$ receives the value T, it follows from the table for $\rightarrow$ that B takes the value T, whence, $A \vDash B$.

The first assertion in (II) follows from the table for $\wedge$, and the second follows from the first by an application of (I).

COROLLARY. $A_1, \cdots, A_{m-1}, A_m \vDash B$ iff $A_1, \cdots, A_{m-1} \vDash A_m \rightarrow B$. More generally, $A_1, \cdots, A_{m-1}, A_m \vDash B$ iff $\vDash A_1 \rightarrow (A_2 \rightarrow (\cdots (A_m \rightarrow B) \cdots))$.

Proof. For $m = 1$, the first assertion is (I) of the theorem. So, assume that $A_1, \cdots, A_{m-1}, A_m \vDash B$ for $m > 1$. Then $\vDash (A_1 \wedge \cdots \wedge A_{m-1}) \wedge A_m \rightarrow B$, according to the theorem. From tautology 8 of Theorem 2.4 and the Corollary to Theorem 2.2, we deduce that $\vDash (A_1 \wedge \cdots \wedge A_{m-1}) \rightarrow (A_m \rightarrow B)$. According to (I) of the theorem, it follows that $A_1 \wedge \cdots \wedge A_{m-1} \vDash A_m \rightarrow B$ and hence, by (II), that $A_1, \cdots, A_{m-1} \vDash A_m \rightarrow B$. The converse is established by reversing the foregoing steps.

Finally, the second assertion follows by repeated application of the first.

Thus, the problem of what statements are valid consequences of others (by the statement calculus) is reduced to the problem of what statements are valid (which accounts for the importance of tautologies). On the other hand, there is something to be said for approaching the concept of valid consequence directly. One reason is the possibility of converting the definition into a working form which resembles that used in mathematics to infer theorems from a set of axioms. Indeed, we can substantiate a working form as a sequence of formulas (the last formula being the desired consequence of the premises) such that the presence of each is justified by a rule, called a **rule of inference** (for the statement calculus). The basis for the rules of inference which we shall introduce is the following theorem.

THEOREM 2.7.

(I) $A_1, A_2, \cdots, A_m \models A_i$ for $i = 1, 2, \cdots, m$.

(II) If $A_1, A_2, \cdots, A_m \models B_j$ for $j = 1, 2, \cdots, p$, and if $B_1, B_2, \cdots, B_p \models C$, then $A_1, A_2, \cdots, A_m \models C$.

Proof. Part (I) is an immediate consequence of the definition of "$A_1, A_2, \cdots, A_m \models B$." For (II) we construct a truth table from the list $P_1, P_2, \cdots, P_n$ of all prime components appearing in at least one of the A's, the B's, and C. Consider any row in which $A_1, A_2, \cdots, A_m$ each receive the value $\top$. Then, by the hypotheses, each B has the value $\top$, and hence C has the value $\top$. That is, for each assignment of values to the P's such that every A takes the value $\top$, formula C receives the value $\top$. This is the desired conclusion.

With this result, a demonstration that a formula B (the conclusion) is a valid consequence of formulas $A_1, A_2, \cdots, A_m$ (the premises) may be presented in the form of a **string** (that is, a finite sequence) of formulas, the last of which is B and such that the presence of each formula E is justified by an application of one of the following rules.

Rule p: The formula E is a premise.

Rule t: There are formulas $A, \cdots, C$ preceding E in the string such that $\models A \wedge \cdots \wedge C \rightarrow E$.

That is, we contend that $A_1, A_2, \cdots, A_m \vDash B$ if we can concoct a string

$$E_1, E_2, \cdots, E_r(= B)$$

of formulas such that either each E is a premise (rule p) or there are preceding formulas in the string such that if C is their conjunction, then $\vDash C \to E$ (rule t). Indeed, assuming that each entry in the displayed sequence can be so justified, we shall prove that

$$A_1, A_2, \cdots, A_m \vDash \text{(any } E \text{ in the sequence).}$$

This is true of E_1 by Theorem 2.7(I). Assume that each of $E_1, E_2, \cdots, E_{k-1}$ is a valid consequence of the A's; we prove that the same is true of the next formula E_k. If E_k is a premise, then Theorem 2.7(I) applies. Otherwise, there are formulas preceding E_k such that if C is their conjunction, then $\vDash C \to E_k$. Let us say

$$\vDash E_{i_1} \wedge E_{i_2} \wedge \cdots \wedge E_{i_s} \to E_k.$$

Then, by Theorem 2.6(II),

$$E_{i_1}, E_{i_2}, \cdots, E_{i_s} \vDash E_k,$$

and, by assumption,

$$A_1, A_2, \cdots, A_m \vDash E_{i_j}, \qquad j = 1, 2, \cdots, s.$$

Hence, by Theorem 2.7(II),

$$A_1, A_2, \cdots, A_m \vDash E_k.$$

We note, finally, that by an application of rule t any tautology may be entered in a derivation. Indeed, if $\vDash D$, then for any formula A we have $\vDash A \to D$. Thus, D may be included in a derivation by an application of rule t wherein we take any premise as the "A."

EXAMPLES B

1. We demonstrate that

$$A \vee B, A \to C, B \to D \vDash C \vee D.$$

An explanation of the numerals on the left is given below.

| $\{1\}$ | (1) $A \to C$ | Rule p |
| $\{1\}$ | (2) $A \vee B \to C \vee B$ | Rule t; $\vDash$ (1) $\to$ (2) by tautology 11. |

{3}	(3) $B \rightarrow D$	Rule p
{3}	(4) $C \vee B \rightarrow C \vee D$	Rule t; $\vDash$ (3) $\rightarrow$ (4) by tautology 11.
{1,3}	(5) $A \vee B \rightarrow C \vee D$	Rule t; $\vDash$ (2) $\wedge$ (4) $\rightarrow$ (5) by tautology 7.
{6}	(6) $A \vee B$	Rule p
{1,3,6}	(7) $C \vee D$	Rule t; $\vDash$ (5) $\wedge$ (6) $\rightarrow$ (7) by tautology 1.

The numbers in parentheses adjacent to each formula serve to designate that formula as well as the line of the derivation in which it
appears. The set of numbers in braces for each line corresponds to the
premises on which the formula in that line depends. That is, the
formula in line n is a valid consequence of the premises designated by
the numbers in braces in that line. Thus, the formula in line 5 is a
valid consequence of the premise in line 1 and the premise in line 3,
and the formula in line 7 is a valid consequence of the premises in
lines 1, 3, and 6, that is, of all the premises. In particular, for a line
which displays a premise there appears in braces at the left just the
number of that line, since such a formula depends on no other line.
Using the brace notation in connection with the numerals on the left
is deliberate in that it suggests that the formula in that line is a valid
consequence of the set of premises designated by those numbers.

We now rewrite the above derivation, incorporating some practical
abbreviations. In this form the reader is called on to supply the tautologies employed.

{1}	(1) $A \rightarrow C$	p
{1}	(2) $A \vee B \rightarrow C \vee B$	1 t
{3}	(3) $B \rightarrow D$	p
{3}	(4) $C \vee B \rightarrow C \vee D$	3 t
{1,3}	(5) $A \vee B \rightarrow C \vee D$	2, 4 t
{6}	(6) $A \vee B$	p
{1,3,6}	(7) $C \vee D$	5, 6 t

2. As a more elaborate illustration we prove that

$$W \vee P \rightarrow I, I \rightarrow C \vee S, S \rightarrow U, \sim C \wedge \sim U \vDash \sim W$$

by the following string of thirteen formulas.

| {1} | (1) $\sim C \wedge \sim U$ | p |

{1}	(2) $\sim U$	1 t
{3}	(3) $S \rightarrow U$	p
{1,3}	(4) $\sim S$	2, 3 t
{1}	(5) $\sim C$	1 t
{1,3}	(6) $\sim C \wedge \sim S$	4, 5 t
{1,3}	(7) $\sim (C \vee S)$	6 t
{8}	(8) $W \vee P \rightarrow I$	p
{9}	(9) $I \rightarrow C \vee S$	p
{8,9}	(10) $W \vee P \rightarrow C \vee S$	8, 9 t
{1,3,8,9}	(11) $\sim (W \vee P)$	7, 10 t
{1,3,8,9}	(12) $\sim W \wedge \sim P$	11 t
{1,3,8,9}	(13) $\sim W$	12 t

We note that the foregoing takes the place of a truth table having $2^6 = 64$ lines for the purpose of verifying that

$$\vDash (W \vee P \rightarrow I) \wedge (I \rightarrow C \vee S) \wedge (S \rightarrow U) \wedge (\sim C \wedge \sim U) \rightarrow \sim W.$$

3. Many theorems in mathematics have the form of a conditional, the assumptions being the axioms of the theory under development. The symbolic form of such a theorem is

$$A_1, A_2, \cdots, A_m \vDash B \rightarrow C,$$

where the A's are the axioms and $B \rightarrow C$ is the consequence asserted. In order to prove such a theorem it is standard practice to adopt B as a further assumption and then infer that C is a valid consequence. Thereby it is implied that

$$A_1, A_2, \cdots, A_m \vDash B \rightarrow C \text{ iff } A_1, A_2, \cdots, A_m, B \vDash C.$$

This is correct according to the Corollary to Theorem 2.6. It is convenient to formulate this as a third rule of inference, the rule of conditional proof, for the statement calculus.

Rule cp: The formula $B \rightarrow C$ is justified in a derivation having $A_1, A_2, \cdots, A_m$ as premises if it has been established that C is a valid consequence of $A_1, A_2, \cdots, A_m$, and B.

As an illustration of the use of this rule we prove that

$$A \rightarrow (B \rightarrow C), \sim D \vee A, B \vDash D \rightarrow C.$$

{1}	(1) $A \rightarrow (B \rightarrow C)$	p
{2}	(2) $\sim D \vee A$	p
{3}	(3) B	p

$\{4\}$	(4) D	p (introducing "D" as an additional premise)
$\{2,4\}$	(5) A	2, 4 t
$\{1,2,4\}$	(6) $B \rightarrow C$	1, 5 t
$\{1,2,3,4\}$	(7) C	3, 6 t
$\{1,2,3\}$	(8) $D \rightarrow C$	4, 7 cp

The usefulness of the braced numbers to show precisely what premises enter into the derivation of the formula in that line is clear.

4. Even if an alleged consequence of a set of premises does not have the form of a conditional, the application of the strategy as described in the preceding example may simplify a derivation. As an illustration we rework the first example, starting with the observation that the conclusion $C \lor D$ is equivalent to $\sim C \rightarrow D$. This suggests adding $\sim C$ as a premise and hoping that D can be derived as a consequence of this and the other premises. An advantage gained thereby is the addition of a simple assumption. The derivation follows.

$\{1\}$	(1) $A \lor B$	p
$\{2\}$	(2) $A \rightarrow C$	p
$\{3\}$	(3) $B \rightarrow D$	p
$\{4\}$	(4) $\sim C$	p
$\{2,4\}$	(5) $\sim A$	2, 4 t
$\{1,2,4\}$	(6) B	1, 5 t
$\{1,2,3,4\}$	(7) D	3, 6 t
$\{1,2,3\}$	(8) $\sim C \rightarrow D$	4, 7 cp
$\{1,2,3\}$	(9) $C \lor D$	8 t

5. Each of the tautological implications in Theorem 2.4 generates a rule of inference, namely, the instance of rule t, which is justified by reference to that tautology alone. For example, tautology 1 in Theorem 2.4 determines the rule

From A and $A \rightarrow B$ to infer B.

This is called the **rule of detachment** or **modus ponens.** In a textbook devoted to logic, names for many rules of inference of this sort will be found. Probably modus ponens is the one used most frequently in derivations.

EXERCISES

1. By an examination of Table VIII in Example A, justify the conclusions drawn in that example.

2. Complete each of the following demonstrations of valid consequence by supplying the tautologies employed and the numbering scheme discussed in the first of Examples B.

(a) $A \rightarrow B, \sim(B \vee C) \vDash \sim A$

$A \rightarrow B$
$\sim(B \vee C)$
$\sim B \wedge \sim C$
$\sim B$
$\sim A$

(c) $(A \wedge B) \vee (C \wedge D)$,
$\qquad A \rightarrow \sim A \vDash C$

$A \rightarrow \sim A$
$\sim A \vee \sim A$
$\sim A$
$\sim A \vee \sim B$
$\sim(A \wedge B)$
$(A \wedge B) \vee (C \wedge D)$
$C \wedge D$
C

(b) $A \rightarrow B, C \rightarrow B, D \rightarrow$
$\qquad A \vee C, D \vDash B$

$D \rightarrow A \vee C$
D
$A \vee C$
$A \rightarrow B$
$C \rightarrow B$
$A \vee C \rightarrow B$
B

(d) $A \rightarrow (C \rightarrow B), \sim D \vee A$,
$\qquad C \vDash D \rightarrow B$

$\sim D \vee A$
D
A
$A \rightarrow (C \rightarrow B)$
$C \rightarrow B$
C
B
$D \rightarrow B$

3. Justify each of the following, using only rules p and t.

(a) $\sim A \vee B, C \rightarrow \sim B \vDash A \rightarrow \sim C$.

(b) $A \rightarrow (B \rightarrow C), (C \wedge D) \rightarrow E, \sim F \rightarrow (D \wedge \sim E) \vDash$
$\qquad\qquad\qquad\qquad\qquad A \rightarrow (B \rightarrow F)$.

(c) $A \vee B \rightarrow C \wedge D, D \vee E \rightarrow F \vDash A \rightarrow F$.

(d) $A \rightarrow (B \wedge C), \sim B \vee D, (E \rightarrow \sim F) \rightarrow \sim D$,
$\qquad\qquad\qquad B \rightarrow (A \wedge \sim E) \vDash B \rightarrow E$.

(e) $(A \rightarrow B) \wedge (C \rightarrow D), (B \rightarrow E) \wedge (D \rightarrow F)$,
$\qquad\qquad\qquad \sim(E \wedge F), A \rightarrow C \vDash \sim A$.

4. Try to shorten your proofs of Exercise 3(a), (b), (c), (d) using rule *cp* (along with rules *p* and *t*).

5. Can the rule of conditional proof to be used to advantage in Exercise 3(e)? Justify your answer.

2.5. The Statement Calculus. Applications

We now turn to some household applications of the theory of inference which we have discussed. Usually the circumstances accompanying the presentation of an argument include the audience having the privilege of accepting or rejecting the contention that some statement B is a valid consequence of statements $A_1, A_2, \cdots, A_m$. In this event, the man who thinks for himself will want to prove either that B is a valid consequence of the A's or that the argument is **invalid,** that is, that there can be made an assignment of truth values to the prime components at hand such that simultaneously each A receives value T, and B receives value F. The most expedient way to cope with the entire matter is this: Assume that B has value F and that each A has value T, and analyze the consequences insofar as necessary assignments of truth values to prime components are concerned. Such an analysis will lead to either a contradiction, which proves that B is a valid consequence of the A's, or an assignment to each prime component such that all assumptions are satisfied, which proves that the argument is invalid.

The foregoing method for proving that some formula is a valid consequence of others undercuts that promoted in the preceding section since it proceeds so quickly. However, the earlier method has (at least pedagogical) merits. For example, it leads to an acquaintance with the tautologies in Theorem 2.4. Instances of these are commonplace in proofs in mathematics, and the reader should learn to recognize them as such. As an illustration, tautology 20 justifies the familiar conclusion that if the contrapositive, $\sim Q \to \sim P$, of $P \to Q$ is a valid consequence of A, then so is $P \to Q$.

EXAMPLES A

1. Consider the following argument.

If I go to my first class tomorrow, then I must get up early, and if I go to the dance tonight, I will stay up late. If I stay up late and get up early, then I will be forced to exist on only five hours of sleep. I simply cannot exist on only five hours of sleep. Therefore, I must either miss my first class tomorrow or not go to the dance.

To investigate the validity of this argument, we symbolize it using letters for prime statements. Let C be "I (will) go to my first class tomorrow," G be "I must get up early," D be "I (will) go to the dance tonight," S be "I will stay up late," and E be "I can exist on five hours of sleep." Then the premises may be symbolized as

$$(C \rightarrow G) \wedge (D \rightarrow S),$$
$$S \wedge G \rightarrow E,$$
$$\sim E,$$

and the desired conclusion as

$$\sim C \vee \sim D.$$

Following the method of analysis suggested above, we assume that $\sim C \vee \sim D$ has value F and that each premise has value T. Then each of C and D must have value T. Further, according to the first premise, both G and S have value T. This and the second premise imply that E has value T. But this contradicts the assumption that the third premise has value T. Thus we have proved that $\sim C \vee \sim D$ is a valid consequence of the premises.

2. Suppose it is asserted that

$$A \rightarrow B, C \rightarrow D, A \vee C \models B \wedge D.$$

Assume that $B \wedge D$ has value F and each premise has value T. The first assumption is satisfied if T is assigned to B and F is assigned to D. Then C has value F, and A has value T. With these assignments, each premise receives value T, and $B \wedge D$ takes value F. Hence the argument is invalid.

Related to the foregoing, but distinct from it, is the question of the consistency of a set of statements which is proposed as the set of premises for an inference. A set $\{A_1, A_2, \cdots, A_m\}$ of statements is **consistent** (within the statement calculus) iff there exists at least one assignment of truth values for the prime components such that the A's simultaneously receive value T. The inconsistency of a set of statements is the denial of its consistency. Thus, $\{A_1, A_2, \cdots, A_m\}$ is an **inconsistent** set iff for every assignment of values to the prime components at least one of the A's receives value F. In brief, $\{A_1, A_2, \cdots, A_m\}$ is consistent if $A_1 \wedge A_2 \wedge \cdots \wedge A_m$ is T for at least one combination of truth-value assignments to the prime components and is inconsistent if $A_1 \wedge A_2 \wedge \cdots \wedge A_m$ is F for all combinations of truth-value assignments to the prime components.

The inconsistency of a set of statements can be established within the framework of the methods described in the preceding section as soon as the following definition is made. A **contradiction** is a formula which always takes the value F (for example, $A \wedge \sim A$).

THEOREM 2.8. A set $\{A_1, A_2, \cdots, A_m\}$ of statements is inconsistent if a contradiction can be derived as a valid consequence of the set.

Proof. Assume that $A_1, A_2, \cdots, A_m \models B \wedge \sim B$ for some formula B. Then $\models A_1 \wedge A_2 \wedge \cdots \wedge A_m \rightarrow B \wedge \sim B$, and the conclusion follows from the truth table for the conditional.

Contradictions also play an important role in the method of **indirect proof** (also called **proof by contradiction** or **reductio ad absurdum proof**). The basis for this type of proof is the following result.

THEOREM 2.9. $A_1, A_2, \cdots, A_m \models B$ if a contradiction can be derived as a valid consequence of $A_1, A_2, \cdots, A_m$ and $\sim B$.

Proof. Assume that $A_1, A_2, \cdots, A_m, \sim B \models C \wedge \sim C$ for some formula C. Then $A_1, A_2, \cdots, A_m \models \sim B \rightarrow C \wedge \sim C$. Consider now an assignment of values to the prime components at hand such that every A receives value T. Then $\sim B \rightarrow C \wedge \sim C$ has value T. This and the fact that $C \wedge \sim C$ receives value F imply that $\sim B$ has value F and hence that B has value T.

EXAMPLES B

1. We illustrate the usefulness of Theorem 2.8 in proving the inconsistency of a set of statements. Such a proof follows the same pattern as one devised to establish the correctness of an argument in all but one respect: in a proof of the correctness of an argument the final line, which is the conclusion, is assigned in advance, whereas, in a proof of

inconsistency the final line is any contradiction. For example, suppose that it is a question of the consistency of a set of statements which may be symbolized as follows:

$$A \leftrightarrow B, \ B \rightarrow C, \ \sim C \lor D, \ \sim A \rightarrow D, \ \sim D.$$

We adopt these as a set of premises and investigate what inferences can be made.

{1}	(1)	$A \leftrightarrow B$	p
{2}	(2)	$B \rightarrow C$	p
{3}	(3)	$\sim C \lor D$	p
{4}	(4)	$\sim A \rightarrow D$	p
{5}	(5)	$\sim D$	p
{4,5}	(6)	$\sim\sim A$	4, 5 t
{4,5}	(7)	A	6 t
{1,2}	(8)	$A \rightarrow C$	1, 2 t
{1,2,4,5}	(9)	C	7, 8 t
{3,5}	(10)	$\sim C$	3, 5 t
{1,2,3,4,5}	(11)	$C \land \sim C$	9, 10 t

We conclude that the set is inconsistent.

2. We could introduce a further rule of inference based on Theorem 2.9. Alternatively, we may employ the rule of conditional proof and the tautology $\models (\sim B \rightarrow C \land \sim C) \rightarrow B$ to justify an indirect proof. As an illustration, we rework the first of Examples A in this section, starting with the negation of the desired conclusion as an additional premise.

(1)	$(C \rightarrow G) \land (D \rightarrow S)$	p
(2)	$S \land G \rightarrow E$	p
(3)	$\sim E$	p
(4)	$\sim(\sim C \lor \sim D)$	p
(5)	$C \land D$	
(6)	C	
(7)	$C \rightarrow G$	
(8)	G	
(9)	$D \rightarrow S$	
(10)	D	
(11)	S	
(12)	$S \land G$	

(13) E
(14) $E \wedge \sim E$
(15) $\sim(\sim C \vee \sim D) \rightarrow E \wedge \sim E$
(16) $\sim C \vee \sim D$

It is left as an exercise to supply the missing details.

EXERCISES

Use the method discussed in this section to prove the validity or invalidity, whichever the case might be, of the arguments in Exercises 1–12 below. For those which are valid, construct a formal proof. In every case use the letters suggested for symbolizing the argument.

1. Either I shall go home or stay and have a drink. I shall not go home. Therefore I shall stay and have a drink. (H,S)

2. If John stays up late tonight, he will be dull tomorrow. If he doesn't stay up late tonight, then he will feel that life is not worth living. Therefore, either John will be dull tomorrow or he will feel that life is not worth living. (S,D,L)

3. Wages will increase only if there is inflation. If there is inflation, then the cost of living will increase. Wages will increase. Therefore, the cost of living will increase. (W,I,C)

4. If 2 is a prime, then it is the least prime. If 2 is the least prime, then 1 is not a prime. The number 1 is not a prime. Therefore, 2 is a prime. (P,L,N)

5. Either John is exhausted or he is sick. If he is exhausted, then he is contrary. He is not contrary. Therefore, he is sick. (E,S,C)

6. If it is cold tomorrow, I'll wear my heavy coat if the sleeve is mended. It will be cold tomorrow, and that sleeve will not be mended. Therefore, I'll not wear my heavy coat. (C,H,S)

7. If the races are fixed or the gambling houses are crooked, then the tourist trade will decline, and the town will suffer. If the tourist trade decreases, then the police force will be happy. The police force is never happy. Therefore, the races are not fixed. (R,H,D,S,P)

8. If the Dodgers win, then Los Angeles will celebrate, and if the White Sox win, Chicago will celebrate. Either the Dodgers will win or the White Sox will win. However, if the Dodgers win, then Chicago will not celebrate, and if the White Sox win, Los Angeles will not celebrate. So, Chicago will celebrate if and only if Los Angeles does not celebrate. (D,L,W,C)

9. Either Sally and Bob are the same age or Sally is older than Bob. If Sally and Bob are the same age, then Nancy and Bob are not the same age. If Sally is older than Bob, then Bob is older than Walter. Therefore, either Nancy and Bob are not the same age or Bob is older than Walter. (S,O,N,W)

10. If 6 is a composite number, then 12 is a composite number. If 12 is a composite number, then there exists a prime greater than 12. If there exists a prime greater than 12, then there exists a composite number greater than 12. If 2 divides 6, then 6 is a composite number. The number 12 is composite. Therefore, 6 is a composite number. (S,W,P,C,D)

11. If I take the bus, then if the bus is late, I'll miss my appointment. If I miss my appointment and start to feel downcast, then I should not go home. If I don't get that job, then I'll start to feel downcast and should go home. Therefore, if I take the bus, then if the bus is late, I will get that job. (B,L,M,D,H,J)

12. If Smith wins the nomination, he will be happy, and if he is happy, he is not a good campaigner. But if he loses the nomination, he will lose the confidence of the party. He is not a good campaigner if he loses the confidence of the party. If he is not a good campaigner, then he should resign from the party. Either Smith wins the nomination or he loses it. Therefore, he should resign from the party. (N,H,C,P,R)

13. Investigate the following sets of premises for inconsistency. If you conclude that a set is inconsistent by assigning truth values, then reaffirm this using Theorem 2.8 and vice versa. Substantiate each assertion of the consistency of a set of premises by suitable truth-value assignments.

(a) $A \rightarrow \sim(B \wedge C)$
$D \vee E \rightarrow G$
$G \rightarrow \sim(H \vee I)$
$\sim C \wedge E \wedge H$

(b) $A \vee B \rightarrow C \wedge D$
$D \vee E \rightarrow G$
$A \vee \sim G$

(c) $(A \rightarrow B) \wedge (C \rightarrow D)$
$(B \rightarrow D) \wedge (\sim C \rightarrow A)$
$(E \rightarrow G) \wedge (G \rightarrow \sim D)$
$\sim E \rightarrow E$

(d) $(A \rightarrow B \wedge C) \wedge (D \rightarrow B \wedge E)$
$(G \rightarrow \sim A) \wedge H \rightarrow I$
$(H \rightarrow I) \rightarrow G \wedge D$
$\sim(\sim C \rightarrow E)$

(e) The contract is fulfilled if and only if the house is completed in February. If the house is completed in February, then we can move in March 1. If we can't move in March 1, then we must pay rent for March. If the contract is not fulfilled, then we must pay rent for March. We will not pay rent for March. (*C,H,M,R*)

14. Give an indirect proof of each of the following arguments.
   (a) The second of Examples B in Section 2.4.
   (b) The third of Examples B in Section 2.4.
   (c) The first of Examples A in this section.
   (d) Exercise 7 above.
   (e) Exercise 11 above.
   (f) Exercise 12 above.

15. Prove that if A, $\sim B \models C$ (a contradiction), then $A \models B$.

2.6. The Predicate Calculus. Symbolizing Everyday Language

The theory of inference supplied by the statement calculus is quite inadequate for mathematics and, indeed, for everyday arguments. For example, from the premises

> Every rational number is a real number,
> 3 is a rational number,

certainly

> 3 is a real number

is justified as a conclusion. Yet the validity of this argument cannot be established within the context of the statement calculus. The reason is that the statement calculus is limited to the structure of sentences in terms of component sentences, and the above inference requires an analysis of sentence structure along the subject–predicate lines that grammarians describe. In other words, the statement calculus does not break down a sentence into sufficiently "fine" constituents for most purposes. On the other hand, with the addition of three additional logical notions, called **terms, predicates,** and **quantifiers,** it has been found that much of everyday and mathematical language can be symbolized in such a way as to make possible an analysis of an argument. We shall describe these three notions in turn.

It is standard practice in mathematics to introduce letters such as

"x" and "y" to reserve a place for names of individual objects. For example, in order to determine those real numbers such that the square of the number minus the number is equal to twelve, one will form the equation $x^2 - x = 12$, thereby regarding "x" as a place holder for the name of any such (initially unknown) number. Again, as it is normally understood, the "x" in such an equation as

$$\sin^2 x + \cos^2 x = 1$$

reserves a place for the name of any real or, indeed, complex number. As it is employed in "$x^2 - x = 12$," one is accustomed to calling "x" an unknown, and in "$\sin^2 x + \cos^2 x = 1$" one is likely to refer to "x" as a variable. The usage we shall make of letters from the latter part of the alphabet in symbolizing everyday language shall be like that just described, that is, as an unknown or a variable. In logic it is customary to employ the word "variable" for either usage, with the decision as to whether "x" is intended to be a variable in the intuitive sense or an unknown being made on the basis of the form of the expression in which it appears. Since, ultimately, we intend to strip all symbols of any meaning whatsoever, it is simplest to do this at the outset for variables. This we do by defining an **individual variable** to be a letter or a letter with a subscript or superscript. Variables constitute one class of terms.

We shall also find use for letters and symbols as names of specific, well-defined objects; that is, we shall use letters and symbols for proper names. Letters and symbols used for this purpose are called **individual constants.** For example, "3" is an individual constant, being a name of the numeral 3. Again, "Winston Churchill" is an individual constant. In order to achieve a compact notation we shall use a letter from the beginning of the alphabet to stand for a proper name if there is no accepted symbol for it. For example, we might let

$$a = \text{Winston Churchill}$$

if we intend to translate the sentence

Winston Churchill was a great statesman

into symbolic form.

Proper names are often rendered by a "description" which we take to be a name which by its own structure unequivocally identifies the object of which it is a name. For example,

The first president of the United States

and

The real number x such that for all real numbers y, $xy = y$

are descriptions. If we let

$$b = \text{George Washington,}$$

then we may write

$$b = \text{The first president of the United States.}$$

Further, we have

$$1 = \text{the real number } x \text{ such that for all } y,\ xy = y.$$

Collectively, individual variables and individual constants (either in the form of proper names or descriptions) are classified as **terms.** The grammatical function of variables is similar to that of pronouns and common nouns in everyday language, and the function of individual constants is similar to the role of proper nouns.

We now turn to the notion of predicates. In grammar a predicate is the word or words in a sentence which express what is said of the subject; for example, "is a real number," "is black," "is envious." In logic the word "predicate" has a broader role than it has in grammar. The basis for this is the observation that if a predicate is supplemented by including a variable as a place-holder for the intended subject (for example, "x is a real number"), the result behaves as a "statement function" in the sense that for each value of x (from an appropriate domain) a statement results. Although "John loves" is not a predicate in grammar, if "x" is introduced as a place-holder for the object (of John's affections), which yields

John loves x,

the result is a statement function in the sense just described. An obvious generalization is at hand, namely, the extension to statement functions of more than one variable. The following are examples.

x is less than y;
x divides y;
z is the sum of x and y.

The upshot is the notion of an **n-place predicate** $P(x_1, x_2, \cdots, x_n)$ as an expression having the quality that on an assignment of values to the variables $x_1, x_2, \cdots, x_n$ from appropriate domains, a statement results. For convenience we include 0 as a value of n, understanding by a 0-place predicate a statement.

We now consider some examples of translations into symbolic form.

EXAMPLES A

1. The sentence

(1)   Every rational number is a real number

may be translated as

(2)   For every x, if x is a rational number, then x is a real number.

In ordinary grammar, "is a real number" is the predicate of (1). In the translation (2) the added predicate "x is a rational number" replaces the common noun "rational number." Using "$Q(x)$" for "x is a rational number" and "$R(x)$" for "x is a real number," we may symbolize (2) as

(3)   For every x, $Q(x) \rightarrow R(x)$.

Further, the statement "3 is a rational number" may be symbolized by

(4) $Q(3)$.

In terms of symbolism available at the moment, (3) and (4) are the translations of the premises of the argument appearing at the beginning of this section.

2. The sentence

                 Some real numbers are rational

we translate as

        For some x, x is a real number and x is a rational number.

Using the predicates introduced above, this may be symbolized as

(5)   For some x, $R(x) \wedge Q(x)$.

3. The sentence

(6)   For some x, $R(x) \rightarrow Q(x)$

should have the same meaning as

(7)   For some x, $\sim R(x) \vee Q(x)$,

since we have merely replaced "$R(x) \rightarrow Q(x)$" by its equivalent "$\sim R(x) \vee Q(x)$." Now (7) may be translated into words as

There is something which is either not a real number or is a
rational number.

Certainly, this statement [which has the same meaning as (6)] does
not have the same meaning as (5). Indeed, as soon as we exhibit an object which is not a real number we must subscribe to (6). In summary,
(6) and (5) have different meanings.

By assumption, on suitable assignments of values to the variables in
a predicate a statement results. For example, if $S(x)$ is "x is a sophomore," this predicate yields the statement "John is a sophomore." A
statement may also be obtained from $S(x)$ by prefixing it with the
phrase "for every x":

(8)   For every x, x is a sophomore.

No doubt, one would choose to rephrase this as

(9)   Everyone is a sophomore.

The phrase "for every x" is called a **universal quantifier.** We regard
"for every x," "for all x," and "for each x" as having the same meaning
and symbolize each by

$$(\forall x) \text{ or } (x).$$

Using this symbol we may symbolize (8) or (9) as

$$(x)S(x).$$

Similarly, prefixing $S(x)$ with the phrase "there exists an x (such
that)" yields a statement which has the same meaning as "There are
sophomores." The phrase "there exists an x" is called an **existential
quantifier.** We regard "there exists an x," "for some x," and "for at
least one x" as having the same meaning, and symbolize each by

$$(\exists x).$$

Thus, "$(\exists x)S(x)$" is the symbolic form of "There are sophomores."

In each of Examples A above a quantifier prefixes not merely a
predicate but a "formula in x" by which we shall understand for the
time being an expression compounded from one-place predicates
$P(x), \cdots$ using sentential connectives. Using the symbol introduced
for the universal quantifier, we can now render "Every rational
number is a real number" in its final form:

(10) $$(x)(Q(x) \rightarrow R(x)).$$

Possibly it has already occurred to the reader that this means simply that $Q \subseteq R$. Indeed, if one recalls the definition of the inclusion relation for sets, it becomes clear that (7) is an instance of that definition. Further, we note that (10) is characteristic of statements of the form "Every so and so is a such and such."

Similarly, the sentence "Some real numbers are rational" may be translated as

(11) $$(\exists x)(R(x) \wedge Q(x)).$$

The meaning of this sentence is simply that $R \cap Q$ is nonempty; that is, it is a symmetrical form of the original sentence. A mistake commonly made by beginners is to infer, since a statement of the form "Every so and so is a such and such" can be symbolized as in (10), that the statement "Some so and so is a such and such" can be symbolized by

$$(\exists x)(R(x) \rightarrow Q(x)).$$

However, as is pointed out in the third of Examples A, this should have the same meaning as

$$(\exists x)(\sim R(x) \vee Q(x)).$$

This should be accepted as true as soon as we exhibit an object which is not a real number. In particular, therefore, it has no relation to what it is intended to say, namely, that some real numbers are rational.

EXAMPLES B

1. The notion of a formula in x, as (vaguely) described above, is the same as that given in Chapter 1. There it was stated that such an expression is often called a property (of x). Associated with a property is a set, according to the intuitive principle of abstraction. Extending in the obvious way the notion of a formula in x to that of a formula in x and y, one can associate with a formula $A(x,y)$ those ordered pairs $\langle a,b \rangle$ such that $A(a,b)$ is true. That is, a formula in x and y may be used to define a binary relation. This being so, formulas in two variables are often called binary relations, those in three variables are called ternary relations, and so on.

2. If $A(x)$ is a formula in x, consider the following four statements.

(a) $(x)A(x)$.   (c) $(x)(\sim A(x))$.
(b) $(\exists x)A(x)$.   (d) $(\exists x)(\sim A(x))$.

We might translate these into words as follows:

(a) Everything has property A.

(b) Something has property A.

(c) Nothing has property A.

(d) Something does not have property A.

Now (d) is the denial of (a), and (c) is the denial of (b), on the basis of everyday meaning. Thus, for example, the existential quantifier may be defined in terms of the universal quantifier by agreeing that "$(\exists x)A(x)$" is an abbreviation for "$\sim(x)(\sim A(x))$."

3. Traditional logic emphasized four basic types of statements involving quantifiers. Illustrations of these along with translations appear below. Two of these translations have been discussed.

All rationals are reals.	$(x)(Q(x) \rightarrow R(x))$.
No rationals are reals.	$(x)(Q(x) \rightarrow \sim R(x))$.
Some rationals are reals.	$(\exists x)(Q(x) \wedge R(x))$.
Some rationals are not reals.	$(\exists x)(Q(x) \wedge \sim R(x))$.

4. If the symbols for negation and a quantifier modify a formula, the order in which they appear is relevant. For example, the translation of

$$\sim(x)(x \text{ is mortal})$$

is "Not everyone is mortal" or "Someone is immortal," whereas the translation of

$$(x)(\sim(x \text{ is mortal}))$$

is "Everyone is immortal."

5. By prefixing a formula in several variables with a quantifier (of either kind) for each variable, a statement results. For example, if it is understood that all variables are restricted to the set of real numbers, then

$$(x)(y)(z)((x + y) + z = x + (y + z))$$

is the statement to the effect that addition is an associative operation. Again,

$$(x)(\exists y)(x^2 - y = y^2 - x)$$

translates into "For every (real number) x there is a (real number) y such that $x^2 - y = y^2 - x$." This is a true statement. Notice, however, that

$$(\exists y)(x)(x^2 - y = y^2 - x),$$

obtained from the foregoing by interchanging the quantifiers, is a different, indeed, a false statement.

6. We supplement the first remark in the preceding example with the observation that a formula in several variables can also be reduced to a statement by substituting values for all occurrences of some variables and applying quantifiers which pertain to the remaining variables. For example, the (false) statement

$$(x)(x < 3)$$

results from the 2-place predicate "$x < y$" by substituting a value for y and quantifying x.

We conclude this section with the remark that there are no mechanical rules for translating sentences from English into the logical notation which has been introduced. In every case one must first decide on the meaning of the English sentence and then attempt to convey that same meaning in terms of predicates, quantifiers, and, possibly, individual constants.

Beginning with the exercises below we shall often omit parentheses when writing predicates. For example, in place of "$A(x)$" we shall write "Ax," and "$A(x,y)$" will be written simply as "Axy."

EXERCISES

1. Let Px be "x is a prime," Ex be "x is even," Ox be "x is odd," and Dxy be "x divides y." Translate each of the following into English.

   (a) $P7$.   (e) $(x)(\sim Ex \rightarrow \sim D2x)$.

   (b) $E2 \wedge P2$.   (f) $(x)(Ex \wedge (y)(Dxy \rightarrow Ey))$.

   (c) $(x)(D2x \rightarrow Ex)$.   (g) $(x)(Px \rightarrow (\exists y)(Ey \wedge Dxy))$.

   (d) $(\exists x)(Ex \wedge Dx6)$.   (h) $(x)(Ox \rightarrow (y)(Py \rightarrow \sim Dxy))$.

   (i) $(\exists x)(Ex \wedge Px) \wedge \sim(\exists x)((Ex \wedge Px) \wedge (\exists y)(x \neq y \wedge Ey \wedge Py))$.

2. Below are twenty sentences in English followed by the same number of sentences in symbolic form. Try to pair the members of the two sets in such a way that each member of a pair is a translation of the other member of the pair.

   (a) All judges are lawyers. (Jx,Lx)

   (b) Some lawyers are shysters. (Sx)

   (c) No judge is a shyster.

   (d) Some judges are old but vigorous. (Ox,Vx)

(e) Judge Jones is neither old nor vigorous. (*j*)
(f) Not all lawyers are judges.
(g) Some lawyers who are politicians are Congressmen. (*Px,Cx*)
(h) No Congressman is not vigorous.
(i) All Congressmen who are old are lawyers.
(j) Some women are both lawyers and Congressmen. (*Wx*)
(k) No woman is both a politician and a housewife. (*Hx*)
(l) There are some women lawyers who are housewives.
(m) All women who are lawyers admire some judge. (*Axy*)
(n) Some lawyers admire only judges.
(o) Some lawyers admire women.
(p) Some shysters admire no lawyer.
(q) Judge Jones does not admire any shyster.
(r) There are both lawyers and shysters who admire Judge Jones.
(s) Only judges admire judges.
(t) All judges admire only judges.

(a)′ $(\exists x)(Wx \land Cx \land Lx)$.
(b)′ $\sim Oj \land \sim Vj$.
(c)′ $(x)(Jx \to \sim Sx)$.
(d)′ $(\exists x)(Wx \land Lx \land Hx)$.
(e)′ $(x)(Ajx \to \sim Sx)$.
(f)′ $(x)(Jx \to Lx)$.
(g)′ $\sim(x)(Lx \to Jx)$.
(h)′ $(x)(Cx \land Ox \to Lx)$.
(i)′ $(\exists x)(Lx \land Sx)$.
(j)′ $(\exists x)(Lx \land Px \land Cx)$.
(k)′ $(x)(Wx \to \sim(Px \land Hx))$.
(l)′ $(x)(Cx \to Vx)$.
(m)′ $(\exists x)(Jx \land Ox \land Vx)$.
(n)′ $(x)(y)(Ayx \land Jx) \to Jy))$.
(o)′ $(\exists x)(Sx \land (y)(Axy \to \sim Ly))$.
(p)′ $(\exists x)(\exists y)(Lx \land Sy \land Axj \land Ayj)$.
(q)′ $(x)(Wx \land Lx \to (\exists y)(Jy \land Axy))$.
(r)′ $(\exists x)(Lx \land (\exists y)(Wy \land Axy))$.
(s)′ $(x)(Jx \to (y)(Axy \to Jy))$.
(t)′ $(\exists x)(Lx \land (y)(Axy \to Jy))$.

2.7. The Predicate Calculus. A Formulation

The examples and exercises of the preceding section serve to substantiate the contention that if the sentential connectives are supplemented with predicates and quantifiers, much of everyday language can be symbolized accurately. Predicate calculus is concerned with a theory of inference based on the structure of sentences in terms of connectives, predicates, and quantifiers. In particular, therefore, it is an extension of the statement calculus. The type we shall discuss admits of quantification of only individual variables. To distinguish this simple type from others, it is usually called **restricted** predicate calculus or predicate calculus of **first-order**. Incidentally, it is not our intention to develop the restricted predicate calculus to the same degree of completeness as we did the statement calculus. Rather, we shall merely formulate it and sketch how it might be developed and applied. A formulation which is comparable to that of the statement calculus in Section 2.3 is our starting point.

We assume that for each of $n = 0, 1, 2, \cdots$ there is given an unspecified number of n-place predicates (or, statement functions of n variables). These we shall denote by such symbols as $P(x,y)$ (to stand for some one 2-place predicate), $P(x,y,z)$ (to stand for some one 3-place predicate which would necessarily represent a predicate different from that symbolized by $P(x,y)$, being a function of a different number of variables), $Q(x,y,z)$ (to stand for another 3-place predicate), R (to stand for some one 0-place predicate, that is, a statement), and so on. It is assumed that the set of all n-place predicates for $n = 1, 2, \cdots$ is nonempty. Henceforth we shall call the given predicates **predicate letters.**

From the given set of predicate letters we generate those expressions which we shall call "formulas (of the predicate calculus)." A **prime formula** is an expression resulting from a predicate letter by the substitution of any variables, not necessarily distinct, for those variables which appear in the predicate letter. For example, some of the prime formulas which the predicate letter $P(x,y,z)$ yields are $P(x,y,z)$, $P(x,y,y)$, $P(y,x,x)$, and $P(u,u,u)$. We extend the set of all prime formulas by adjoining all of those expressions which can be formed using, repeatedly, and in all possible ways, the sentential connectives and quantifiers. Precisely, we extend the set of all prime formulas to the smallest set such that each of the following holds. If A and B are members of the set, then so are $\sim(A)$, $(A) \wedge (B)$, $(A) \vee (B)$, $(A) \rightarrow (B)$, and $(A) \leftrightarrow (B)$. Also, if A is a member of the set and x is a variable, then $(x)A$ and $(\exists x)A$ are members of the set. The members of this extended set are called **formulas.** Those which are not prime formulas are called **composite formulas.**

Parentheses are inserted automatically in a formula, but in some cases are unnecessary. (Indeed, the sole purpose of such lavish use of parentheses is to make possible the formulation of a mechanical procedure for demonstrating that some juxtaposition of symbols is a formula.) In other cases parentheses can be omitted by the same conventions established earlier. We extend those conventions by agreeing that quantifiers, along with $\sim$, have the least possible scope. For example, $(\exists x)A \vee B$ stands for $((\exists x)(A)) \vee (B)$.

The foregoing description is vague only with respect to the nature of a predicate letter. From the standpoint of the theory of the first-order predicate calculus, the nature of predicate letters is irrelevant, for there they are treated in a purely formal way, that is, simply as certain strings of letters, parentheses, and commas. From the standpoint of the applications, the vagueness is deliberate, for thereby versatility is achieved. The examples which follow may serve to substantiate this assertion. Each example describes the initial steps which one might take in axiomatizing a mathematical theory.

EXAMPLES

1. Suppose that a practitioner of the axiomatic method were to set out to reconstruct the set theory of Chapter 1 as an axiomatic theory. After analyzing how that subject matter was developed he might conclude that all concepts stemmed from the membership relation, that is, the 2-place predicate "is a member of." This might motivate the practitioner to set up a system of the type introduced above, one having a single predicate letter $\in(x,y)$ intended to denote the membership relation. Of course, the intended interpretation of individual variables would be as sets. The prime formulas of the system would consist of all expressions of the form $\in(x,y)$ or, using more suggestive notation, $x \in y$. Then, for convenience, further predicates could be introduced by definition. Following are some instances.

$x \notin y$ for $\sim(x \in y)$;
$x \subseteq y$ for $(a)(a \in x \to a \in y)$;
$x = y$ for $(x \subseteq y) \wedge (y \subseteq x)$;
$x \neq y$ for $\sim(x = y)$;
$x \subset y$ for $(x \subseteq y) \wedge (x \neq y)$.

The next step would be the adoption of certain formulas as axioms.

2. As every high school student knows, the basic ingredients of elementary geometry are "points," "lines," and the relation of incidence, "_____ lies on _____." In formulating an axiomatic theory intended to have intuitive geometry as an interpretation, one might choose as primitive terms a list of individual variables (intended to range over points and lines), two 1-place predicate letters, $P(x)$ and $L(x)$, and one 2-place predicate latter, $I(x,y)$. These might be read, in turn, "x is a point," "x is a line," and "x is on y." Among the axioms might appear the following:

$$(\exists x)P(x), (\exists x)L(x),$$
$$(x)(y)(I(x,y) \leftrightarrow I(y,x)),$$
$$(x)(P(x) \to (\exists y)(L(y) \wedge I(x,y))).$$

3. As the first step in axiomatizing the theory of partially ordered sets as described in Chapter 1, one might introduce as the primitive terms a list of individual variables and two 2-place predicate letters, $= (x,y)$ and $< (x,y)$. Then the prime formulas would consist of all expressions of the form $x = y$ and $x < y$, using more familiar notation. As nonlogical axioms (that is, those axioms which serve as a basis for the intended mathematical structure) for the theory we might then take

$$(x)(x = x), (x)(y)(x = y \to y = x), (x)(y)(z)(x = y \wedge y = z \to x = z)$$

(which mean that $=$ is an equivalence relation),

$$(x)(y)(z)(x = y \wedge x < z \to y < z), (x)(y)(z)(x = y \wedge z < x \to z < y)$$

(which assert that "equals may be substituted for equals"), and, finally,

$$(x) \sim (x < x), (x)(y)(z)(x < y \wedge y < z \to x < z)$$

(which establishes $<$ as an ordering relation).

As part of the formulation of the predicate calculus there must be introduced definitions for distinguishing between the circumstances in which a variable is intended to play the role of a variable or an unknown in the intuitive sense. As a preliminary to this we define the **scope** of a quantifier occurring in a formula as the formula to which the quantifier applies. A possible ambiguity is removed by use of parentheses. Below are several examples illustrating the scope of the quantifier "(x)." The scope is indicated by the line underneath.

$$(x)\underline{P(x)} \wedge Q(x);$$
$$(\exists y)(x)\underline{(P(x,y) \rightarrow (z)Q(z))};$$
$$(x)\underline{(y)(P(x,y) \wedge Q(y,z))} \wedge (\exists x)P(x,y);$$
$$(x)\underline{(P(x) \wedge (\exists x)Q(x,z) \rightarrow (\exists y)R(x,y))} \vee Q(x,y).$$

It is now possible to give the key definitions in connection with the matter at hand. An occurrence of a variable in a formula is **bound** iff this occurrence is within the scope of a quantifier employing that variable or is the explicit occurrence in that quantifier. An occurrence of a variable is **free** iff this occurrence of the variable is not bound. For example, in

$$(x)P(x,y)$$

both occurrences of x are bound, and the single occurrence of y is free. Again, in the formula

$$(\exists y)(x)(P(x,y) \rightarrow (z)Q(z))$$

each occurrence of every variable is bound. A variable is **free in a formula** iff at least one occurrence of it is free, and a variable is **bound in a formula** iff at least one occurrence of it is bound. A variable may be both free and bound in a formula. This is true of z in the formula

$$(z)(P(z) \wedge (\exists x)Q(x,z) \rightarrow (\exists y)R(z,y)) \vee Q(z,x).$$

If a variable is free in a formula, then, on an assignment of meaning to the predicates involved, that variable behaves as an unknown in the familiar sense, since the formula becomes a statement about that variable. The formulas $x < 7$ and $(\exists y)(y < x)$, in each of which x is free, serve to illustrate this point. The formula

$$(\exists y)(y < x) \wedge (x)(x > 0),$$

wherein the first occurrence of x is free and the other two are bound, illustrates the remark that insofar as meaning is concerned, the free and bound occurrences of the same variable in the same formula have nothing to do with each other. Indeed, the formula $(x)(x > 0)$ is simply a statement and has the same meaning as $(u)(u > 0)$ and $(w)(w > 0)$.

In bound occurrences in a formula a variable behaves like a variable in the intuitive sense. For example, in

$$(x)(x^2 - 1 = (x - 1)(x + 1))$$

all occurrences of x are bound and, clearly, x serves as a variable. That x in the formula

$$(\exists x)(y \neq x)$$

serves as a variable is made more plausible on recalling that this formula has the same meaning as

$$\sim(x)\sim(y \neq x).$$

In conclusion, we note that it is now possible to give a precise definition of the word "statement." A **statement** is a formula which has no free variables.

EXERCISES

1. List the bound and the free occurrences of each variable in each of the following formulas.

(a) $(x)P(x)$.

(b) $(x)P(x) \rightarrow P(y)$.

(c) $P(x) \rightarrow (\exists x)Q(x)$.

(d) $(\exists x)A(x) \wedge B(x)$.

(e) $(\exists x)(y)(P(x) \wedge Q(y)) \rightarrow (x)R(x)$.

(f) $(\exists x)(\exists y)(P(x,y) \wedge Q(z))$.

2. Using the letters indicated for predicates, and whatever symbols of arithmetic (for example, "$+$" and "$<$") may be needed, translate the following.

(a) If the product of a finite number of factors is equal to zero, then at least one of the factors is equal to zero. (Px for "x is a product of a finite number of factors," and Fxy for "x is a factor of y.")

(b) Every common divisor of a and b divides their greatest common divisor. (Fxy for "x is a factor of y," and $Gxyz$ for "z is the greatest common divisor of x and y.")

(c) For each real number x there is a larger real number y. (Rx)

(d) There exist real numbers x, y, and z such that the sum of x and y is greater than the product of x and z.

(e) For every real number x there exists a y such that for every z, if the sum of z and 1 is less than y, then the sum of x and 2 is less than 4.

3. An **abelian group** may be defined as a (nonempty) set A together with a binary operation $+$ in A which is associative, commutative, and such that for given x and y in A the equation $x + z = y$ always possesses a solution z in A. A familiar example is that of $\mathbb{Z}$ with ordinary addition as the operation.

A formulation within the predicate calculus can be given by taking as primitive terms a list of variables, a 2-place predicate latter $= (x,y)$, and a 3-place predicate letter $S(x,y,z)$. The prime formula $x = y$ is read "x equals y," and the prime formula $S(x,y,z)$ is read "z is the sum of x and y." As axioms we take the following formulas.

$(x)(x = x).$
$(x)(y)(x = y \rightarrow y = x).$
$(x)(y)(z)(x = y \land y = z \rightarrow x = z).$
$(u)(v)(w)(x)(y)(z)(S(u,v,w) \land u = x \land y = v \land w = z \rightarrow S(x,y,z)).$
$(x)(y)(\exists z)S(x,y,z).$
$(x)(y)(z)(w)(S(x,y,z) \land S(x,y,w) \rightarrow z = w).$
$(u)(v)(w)(x)(y)(z)(S(u,v,w) \land S(w,x,y) \land S(v,x,z) \rightarrow S(u,z,y)).$
$(x)(y)(z)(S(x,y,z) \rightarrow S(y,x,z)).$
$(x)(y)(\exists z)S(x,z,y).$

Write a paragraph in support of the contention that, collectively, these axioms do serve to define abelian groups.

2.8. The Predicate Calculus. Validity

The system described in the preceding section is essentially the common starting point in the formulation of various predicate calculi. Distinguishing features of the classical predicate calculus (which is our concern) include further assumptions which extend the one assumption made in Section 2.3 for the statement calculus, namely, that with each prime formula there is associated exactly one of T and F. The corresponding assumption about a prime formula in the sense of the predicate calculus is much more complicated. We shall introduce it in several steps. First, it is assumed that with the system described in the preceding section there is associated a nonempty set D, called the **domain,** such that each individual variable ranges over D. Further, it is assumed that with each n-place predicate letter there is associated a **logical function,** that is, a function on D^n into $\{T,F\}$. (For 0-place predicates the associated function is assumed to be a constant, one of T or F.) Finally, it is assumed that a truth-value assignment to a prime formula $P(y_1, y_2, \cdots, y_n)$ can be made, relative to an assignment of an element in D to each distinct variable among $y_1, y_2, \cdots, y_n$, in the following way. If to y_i is assigned d_i in D and if to the predicate letter $P(x_1, x_2, \cdots, x_n)$ is assigned $\lambda: D^n \rightarrow \{T,F\}$, then the truth value of $P(y_1, y_2, \cdots, y_n)$ is $\lambda(d_1, d_2, \cdots, d_n)$. For example, if $P(x,y,x)$ is the prime formula and λ is assigned to $P(x,y,z)$, then the truth value of $P(x,y,x)$, relative to the assignment of x to a and y to b, is $\lambda(a,b,a)$.

For the theory of the statement calculus, that one of T and F which is assigned to a prime formula is assumed to be irrelevant. In the predicate calculus this is extended to the assumption that the theory is independent of the domain D and the assignment of functions to predicate letters.

The foregoing is the basis of the **valuation procedure** for a formula C of the predicate calculus. For this it is assumed that (i) a domain D is given, (ii) a function is assigned to each predicate letter appearing in C, and (iii) to each distinct free variable in C is assigned a value in D. Collectively, these constitute an **assignment** to C. A truth value is assigned to C by a procedure which parallels the formation of C:

(I) If $P(y_1, y_2, \cdots, y_n)$ is a prime formula in C and λ is assigned to $P(x_1, x_2, \cdots, x_n)$ and d_i is assigned to y_i, then the truth value of $P(y_1, y_2, \cdots, y_n)$ is $\lambda(d_1, d_2, \cdots, d_n)$.

(II) For a given assignment of values to the predicate letters and free variables of $\sim A$, the value of $\sim A$ is F if the value of A is T, and the value of $\sim A$ is T if the value of A is F. Similarly, for a given assignment of values to the predicate letters and free variables of $A \vee B$, $A \wedge B$, $A \rightarrow B$, and $A \leftrightarrow B$, the truth tables from the statement calculus apply.

(III) For a given assignment of values to the predicate letters and free variables of $(x)A$, the value of $(x)A$ is T if the value of A is T for every assignment to x, and the value of $(x)A$ is F if the value of A is F for at least one assignment to x. For a given assignment of values to the predicate letters and free variables of $(\exists x)A$, the value of $(\exists x)A$ is T if the value of A is T for at least one value of x, and otherwise it is F.

As an illustration, we consider the problem of the assignment of truth values to the formula

$$(x)(P(x) \to Q) \lor (Q \land P(y)).$$

Although the domain D is fixed, it is unknown. Suppose $D = \{a,b\}$. By assumption there is associated with $P(x)$ a logical function on D into $\{\mathsf{T},\mathsf{F}\}$ and with Q a truth value. Further, the free variable y may assume any value in D. The possible logical functions which may be associated with $P(x)$ are tabulated below.

x	$\lambda_1(x)$	$\lambda_2(x)$	$\lambda_3(x)$	$\lambda_4(x)$
a	T	T	F	F
b	T	F	T	F

The possible values which may be associated with Q are T and F, and to y may be assigned the value a or b. Thus, we may fill out a table with $16(= 4 \cdot 2 \cdot 2)$ entries exhibiting the truth-value assignment in all possible cases:

$P(x)$	Q	y	$(x)(P(x) \to Q) \lor (Q \land P(y))$		
$\lambda_1(x)$	T	a	T	T	T
$\lambda_1(x)$	T	b	T	T	T
$\lambda_1(x)$	F	a	F	F	F
$\lambda_1(x)$	F	b	F	F	F
$\lambda_2(x)$	T	a	T	T	T
$\lambda_2(x)$	T	b	T	T	F
$\lambda_2(x)$	F	a	F	F	F
$\lambda_2(x)$	F	b	F	F	F
$\lambda_3(x)$	T	a	T	T	F
$\lambda_3(x)$	T	b	T	T	T
$\lambda_3(x)$	F	a	F	F	F
$\lambda_3(x)$	F	b	F	F	F
$\lambda_4(x)$	T	a	T	T	F
$\lambda_4(x)$	T	b	T	T	F
$\lambda_4(x)$	F	a	T	T	F
$\lambda_4(x)$	F	b	T	T	F

The entries appearing under $P(x)$, Q, and y in a fixed row make up an assignment to the formula under consideration. The details of the computation accompanying the assignment given in the ninth row of the table are as follows. First we substitute the assignments into the formula to obtain

$$(x)(\lambda_3(x) \rightarrow \mathsf{T}) \vee (\mathsf{T} \wedge \lambda_3(a)).$$

In order to evaluate $(x)(\lambda_3(x) \rightarrow \mathsf{T})$ we must compute $\lambda_3(x) \rightarrow \mathsf{T}$ as a logical function of x. The table for this is given below.

x	$\lambda_3(x) \rightarrow \mathsf{T}$	
a	F	T T
b	T	T T

Since the value of the conditional is T for all assignments to x in D, $(x)(\lambda_3(x) \rightarrow \mathsf{T})$ is evaluated as T. Since $\lambda_3(a) = \mathsf{F}$, the value of $\mathsf{T} \wedge \lambda_3(a)$ is F. Finally, by the table for $\vee$, the value of the entire formula is T. We summarize these steps in tabular form:

$$(x)(P(x) \rightarrow Q) \vee (Q \wedge P(y))$$
$$(x)(\lambda_3(x) \rightarrow \mathsf{T}) \vee (\mathsf{T} \wedge \lambda_3(a))$$
$$\mathsf{T} \qquad\qquad \vee (\mathsf{T} \wedge \mathsf{F})$$
$$\mathsf{F}$$
$$\mathsf{T}$$

Our description of the predicate calculus is intended to parallel that of the statement calculus beginning with Section 2.3. So far, for the predicate calculus, we have introduced the symbols to be employed, given the definition of a formula, and described a valuation procedure. We imitate the next step in the earlier theory by defining validity in the predicate calculus. A formula is **valid in a given domain** iff it takes the value T for every assignment to the predicate letters and free variables in it. A formula is **valid** iff it is valid in every domain. For "A is valid" we shall write

$$\models A.$$

It is appropriate to use the same terminology and symbolism as before, since this definition of validity is an extension of the earlier one. It is obvious that to establish the validity of some formula, truth tables must give way to reasoning processes. On the other hand, to establish nonvalidity, just one D and one assignment based on this domain will suffice. For example, the fourth line of the above table demonstrates that the formula considered there is not valid. The ease with which the validity of some formulas can be established may come as a surprise.

EXAMPLES A

1. Let us illustrate the assignment of functions to predicate letters in an application of the predicate calculus. Suppose that Z is the domain and that we are told that $P(x,y,z)$ is to be interpreted as "z is the sum of x and y." Then to this predicate letter we would assign the function $\lambda: Z^3 \to \{T,F\}$ such that $\lambda(a,b,c) = T$ if $a + b = c$, and $\lambda(a,b,c) = F$ otherwise. If, on the other hand, we are told that $P(x,y,z)$ is to be interpreted as "z is the product of x and y," then we would define $\lambda(a,b,c)$ to be T if $ab = c$, and to be F otherwise.

2. We prove that
$$\vDash (x)P(x) \to P(y).$$
A prerequisite for the formula to take the value F is that $P(y)$ receive the value F for some assignment in some domain. But in that event, $(x)P(x)$ receives the value F. Hence, $(x)P(x) \to P(y)$ always receives the value T.

3. Let us prove that
$$\vDash P(y) \to (\exists x)P(x).$$
As in the preceding example we need concern ourselves only with assignments in some domain D such that $(\exists x)P(x)$ takes value F. This is the case iff $P(x)$ receives value F as x ranges over D. But then $P(y)$ must receive the value F.

4. Let us establish the nonvalidity of the formula $(\exists x)P(x) \to (x)P(x)$. Let D contain at least two individuals, a and b. Assign to $P(x)$ a logical function λ such that $\lambda(a) = T$ and $\lambda(b) = F$. Then $(\exists x)P(x)$ receives the value T and $(x)P(x)$ receives the value F. Hence, the entire formula receives the value F.

5. A proof that
$$\vDash (x)P(x) \lor (x)Q(x) \to (x)(P(x) \lor Q(x))$$
may be given as follows. Suppose that the consequent takes the value F for an assignment λ_1, λ_2, and a to $P(x)$, $Q(x)$, and x, respectively. Then, for this assignment, $P(x) \lor Q(x)$ takes the value F. Hence, $\lambda_1(a) = F$ and $\lambda_2(a) = F$, from which it follows that $(x)P(x)$ and $(x)Q(x)$, and hence their disjunction, each take the value F.

We turn now to the question of general methods for proving validity, looking first at what we can take over from the statement calculus. Theorem 2.2 (with "*A* eq *B*" now assigned a meaning in terms of our present valuation procedure) and Theorem 2.3 carry over unchanged. The proofs employ essentially the earlier reasoning. The substance of Theorem 2.1 is the possibility of proving validity of a formula without dissecting it into prime components. This same technique has applications in the predicate calculus. To proceed with our first illustration, let us call a formula of the predicate calculus **prime for the statement calculus** if no sentential connectives appear in it. In terms of the composition of a formula from such prime formulas we can introduce the notion of tautology into the predicate calculus. For example, $P(x) \to P(x)$ is a tautology, and we may recognize tautologies (for example, $A \to A$) even when the prime formulas are not displayed. Clearly, a tautology is a valid formula. In particular, Theorem 2.4 holds for the predicate calculus.

In order to illustrate further the technique under discussion some definitions are required. To **substitute** a variable y for a variable x in a formula A means to replace each free occurrence of x in A by an occurrence of y. If y is to be substituted for x in A, it is convenient to introduce a composite notation such as "$A(x)$" for the substituend and then write "$A(y)$" for the result of the substitution. Such notation as "$A(x)$" for the formula A is used solely to show the dependence of A on x and is not to be confused with the notation for predicate letters; indeed, we do not require that x actually occur free in A and do not exclude the possibility that $A(x)$ may contain free variables other than x. In the future we shall often use such notations as "$A(x)$" or "$A(x,y)$" instead of "A" when we are interested in the dependence of A on a variable x or variables x and y, whether or not we plan to make a substitution. Let us we consider an example. If $A(x)$ is

$$(1) \qquad (x = 1) \wedge (\exists y)(y \neq x),$$

then, clearly, $A(y)$ says something different about y than $A(x)$ says about x. The reason is that the occurrence of x in $(\exists y)(y \neq x)$ is free, whereas an occurrence of y in the same position is bound. In everyday mathematics we are not likely to make a substitution which changes the meaning of a formula. A safeguard against inappropriate substitutions in purely formal situations can be given. A formula $A(x)$ is **free**

for y if no free occurrence of x in $A(x)$ is in the scope of a quantifier (y) or $(\exists y)$. For example, if $A(x)$ is $P(x,y) \wedge (y)Q(y)$, then it is free for y, whereas if $A(x)$ is (1), above, then it is not free for y. If substitutions for x in $A(x)$ are restricted to variables y such that $A(x)$ is free for y, difficulties of the sort mentioned are avoided.

We turn now to the third of Examples A above where we proved that $\vDash P(y) \rightarrow (\exists x)P(x)$ for a predicate letter $P(x)$. Using the same reasoning we can prove that $\vDash A(y) \rightarrow (\exists x)A(x)$, where $A(x)$ is any formula which is free for y. The computation of the value of the formula at hand for a given assignment consists of (i) the computation of a value of the logical function assigned to A, and (ii) the computation of the value of the whole formula. The second step will coincide with that by which the value of $P(y) \rightarrow (\exists x)P(x)$ is computed for some assignment; this, as we have seen, is always $\top$. In general, although a formula A may contain several prime formulas, we may consider A as a prime formula and speak of "the logical function assigned to A." We state the result just derived along with a companion valid formula as our next theorem.

THEOREM 2.10. Let $A(x)$ be a formula which is free for y. Then

    (I) $\vDash (x)A(x) \rightarrow A(y)$,
    (II) $\vDash A(y) \rightarrow (\exists x)A(x)$.

COROLLARY. If $\vDash (x)A(x)$, then $\vDash A(x)$.

Proof. We apply (I) of the theorem, taking x as the y to obtain $\vDash (x)A(x) \rightarrow A(x)$. Now assume that $\vDash (x)A(x)$. Then we may conclude that $\vDash A(x)$ by the extension of Theorem 2.3 mentioned above.

THEOREM 2.11. Let x be any variable, B be any formula not containing any free occurrence of x, and $A(x)$ be any formula. Then
    (I) If $\vDash B \rightarrow A(x)$, then $\vDash B \rightarrow (x)A(x)$.
    (II) If $\vDash A(x) \rightarrow B$, then $\vDash (\exists x)A(x) \rightarrow B$.

Proof. Assume that $\vDash B \rightarrow A(x)$. Let D be any domain and for this domain consider any assignment α to the formula $B \rightarrow (x)A(x)$. Note that since x does not occur free in either B or $(x)A(x)$, α does not include an assignment of a value in D to x. For α, B takes either the value F or T. If B takes the value F, then $B \rightarrow (x)A(x)$ takes the value T. If B takes the value T, then this is still the case when α is extended to include any assignment of a value in D to x. Hence, for α so extended, $A(x)$ receives the value T, since, by assumption, $B \rightarrow A(x)$ has value T. That is, for each assignment to x along with the given assignment α, $(x)A(x)$ receives the value T. It follows that $\vDash B \rightarrow (x)A(x)$.

The proof of (II) is similar and is left as an exercise.

COROLLARY. If $\vDash A(x)$, then $\vDash (x)A(x)$.

Proof. Assume that $\vDash A(x)$. Since $\vDash B \rightarrow (C \rightarrow B)$, if P is any 0-place predicate letter, then $\vDash A(x) \rightarrow (P \vee \sim P \rightarrow A(x))$. Hence, $\vDash P \vee \sim P \rightarrow A(x)$ by Theorem 2.3. By (I) of the above theorem, it follows that $\vDash P \vee \sim P \rightarrow (x)A(x)$. Finally, since $\vDash P \vee \sim P$, another application of Theorem 2.3 gives $\vDash (x)A(x)$.

An illustration in familiar terms of the above corollary is this. A proof of "For all real numbers x, $\sin^2 x + \cos^2 x = 1$" begins by regarding x as some unknown (but fixed) real number. After proving that, for this x, $\sin^2 x + \cos^2 x = 1$, it is argued that since x is *any* real number, the assertion follows. Note that this involves the transition from the consideration of x as a free variable to that of a bound variable.

In the next theorem are listed some basic valid formulas. Since the formulas of Theorem 2.4 extend to the predicate calculus, we continue the numbering used there to emphasize that we are introducing additional valid formulas for the predicate calculus.

THEOREM 2.12. Let x and y be distinct variables, $A(x)$, $B(x)$, and $A(x,y)$ be any formulas, and A be any formula not containing any free occurrences of x. Then

33. $\vDash (\exists x)(\exists y)A(x,y) \leftrightarrow (\exists y)(\exists x)A(x,y)$.
      33′. $\vDash (x)(y)A(x,y) \leftrightarrow (y)(x)A(x,y)$.
34. $\vDash (\exists x)A(x) \leftrightarrow \sim(x)\sim A(x)$.
      34′. $\vDash (x)A(x) \leftrightarrow \sim(\exists x)\sim A(x)$.
35. $\vDash \sim(\exists x)A(x) \leftrightarrow (x)\sim A(x)$.
      35′. $\vDash \sim(x)A(x) \leftrightarrow (\exists x)\sim A(x)$.
36. $\vDash (\exists x)(y)A(x,y) \rightarrow (y)(\exists x)A(x,y)$.

37. $\models (\exists x)(A(x) \lor B(x)) \leftrightarrow (\exists x)A(x) \lor (\exists x)B(x)$.

       37'. $\models (x)(A(x) \land B(x)) \leftrightarrow (x)A(x) \land (x)B(x)$.

38. $\models (x)A(x) \lor (x)B(x) \rightarrow (x)(A(x) \lor B(x))$.

       38'. $\models (\exists x)(A(x) \land B(x)) \rightarrow (\exists x)A(x) \land (\exists x)B(x)$.

39. $\models (\exists x)(A \lor B(x)) \leftrightarrow A \lor (\exists x)B(x)$.

       39'. $\models (x)(A \land B(x)) \leftrightarrow \models A \land (x)B(x)$.

40. $\models (x)(A \lor B(x)) \leftrightarrow A \lor (x)B(x)$.

       40'. $\models (\exists x)(A \land B(x)) \leftrightarrow A \land (\exists x)B(x)$.

The proofs of the validity of these formulas are left as exercises. That some of the formulas are valid should be highly plausible on the basis of meaning; formulas 33 and 33', which mean that existential (or universal) quantifiers can be interchanged at will, are in this category. Again, formulas 34 and 34', which describe how an existential quantifier can be expressed in terms of a universal quantifier and vice versa, were discussed in the preceding section. Formulas 35 and 35' provide rules for transferring $\sim$ across quantifiers. Formulas 37, 37', 38, and 38' are concerned with transferring quantifiers across $\lor$ and $\land$ in general, and formulas 39, 39', 40, and 40' treat special cases of such transfers.

EXAMPLES B

1. We consider some practical illustrations of the use of formulas 35 and 35' in arithmetic. That is, take as the domain D the set of natural numbers. Further, let $<$ and $+$ have their familiar meanings; thus $<(x,y)$ is a 2-place predicate letter, and $+(x,y,z)$ is a 3-place one. The (true) statement "There does not exist a greatest natural number" may be symbolized by

$$(x)(\exists y)(x < y).$$

Its negation,

$$\sim(x)(\exists y)(x < y),$$

may be rewritten, using 35', as

$$(\exists x)\sim((\exists y)(x < y)).$$

In turn, using 35, this may be rewritten as

$$(\exists x)(y) \sim (x < y) \text{ or } (\exists x)(y)(x \geq y).$$

In English this last formula reads "There exists a greatest natural number."

The (false) statement "For every pair m,n of natural numbers there is a natural number p such that $m + p = n$" may be symbolized by

$$(m)(n)(\exists p)(m + p = n).$$

Its negation may be transformed into

$$(\exists m)(\exists n)(p)(m + p \neq n).$$

The reader can translate this into acceptable English.

2. Take for D the set $\underline{R}$ of real numbers. The definition of continuity of a function f at a, namely, "f is continuous at a iff for every $\epsilon > 0$ there exists a $\delta > 0$ such that for all x, if $|x - a| < \delta$, then $|f(x) - f(a)| < \epsilon$" can be translated into the symbolic form

$$(\epsilon)(\epsilon > 0 \rightarrow ((\exists \delta)(\delta > 0 \wedge (x)(|x - a| < \delta \rightarrow |f(x) - f(a)| < \epsilon)))).$$

This can be shortened considerably using the notion of **restricted quantification**, which in practical terms amounts to restricting the range of ϵ and δ to the set $\underline{R}^+$. Then the above may be contracted to

$$(\epsilon)(\exists \delta)(x)(|x - a| < \delta \rightarrow |f(x) - f(a)| < \epsilon).$$

With mild restrictions, the valid formulas of Theorem 2.12 remain valid when some quantifiers are restricted. This makes it possible, for example, to obtain the negation of complicated formulas quickly and in greatly abbreviated form. As an illustration, the reader is asked to form the negation of the original formula above and show that, in terms of restricted quantifiers, it reduces to the negation of the abbreviation of the original formula, which is

$$(\exists \epsilon)(\delta)(\exists x)(|x - a| < \delta \wedge |f(x) - f(a)| \geq \epsilon).$$

EXERCISES

1. For a domain of two elements construct a truth table for the formula $(x)(P \vee Q(x)) \leftrightarrow P \vee (x)Q(x)$.

2. Prove that the formula in the fourth of Examples A is valid in a domain consisting of one element.

3. Establish the validity of formulas 34, 35, and 36 in Theorem 2.12, regarding all constituent formulas as primes.

4. Establish the validity of formulas 37, 38, and 39 in Theorem 2.12, regarding all constituent formulas as primes.

5. Supply an example to show that the converse of formula 36 in Theorem 2.12 is nonvalid.

6. Prove Theorem 2.11(II).

7. As in the first of Examples B, let us take for D the set of natural numbers. Using Theorem 2.12, justify the equivalence of the lefthand and righthand members of each of the following pairs of formulas.

(a) $(\exists x)(y) \sim (y > x)$, $(\exists x) \sim (\exists y)(y > x)$.

(b) $(\exists x)(y)(y > x \lor \sim(y > 0))$, $(\exists x)(y)(y > 0 \to y > x)$.

(c) $(x)(\exists y)(\exists z)(x < y \land z^2 > y)$, $(x)(\exists y)(x < y \land (\exists z)(z^2 > y))$.

8. Let $a_0, a_1, \cdots, a_n, \cdots$ be a sequence of real numbers. Using restricted quantification, translate into symbolic form

(a) the assertion that a is the limit of the sequence;

(b) the assertion that the sequence has a limit;

(c) the assertion that the sequence is a Cauchy sequence (that is, given $\epsilon > 0$ there exists a positive integer k such that if $n, m > k$, then $|a_n - a_m| < \epsilon$).

9. Write the negation of each of the formulas obtained in the preceding exercise.

10. With $\underline{R}$ as domain, translate each of the following statements into symbolic form, write the negation of each (transferring $\sim$ past the quantifiers), and translate each resulting formula into English.

(a) For $x, y \in \underline{R}$ and $z \in \underline{R}^+$, $xz = yz$ implies $x = y$.

(b) The number a is the least upper bound of $A \subseteq \underline{R}$.

(c) The set A has a greatest element.

2.9. The Predicate Calculus. Valid Consequence

The concept of valid consequence for the predicate calculus is an extension of that for the statement calculus as given in Section 2.4. In this extension, statement letters give way to predicate letters, and assignments of truth values give way to the more elaborate assignments of the predicate calculus. In addition, a further ingredient appears for the first time, namely, the possibility that an assumption formula contains a free occurrence of a variable. For example, in a theorem in arithmetic, an assumption may have the form "Let x be an integer greater than 0" or "Suppose that x is divisible by 3." An examination of how such an x is "treated" in a proof, reveals that it is regarded as a constant; that is, it is regarded as a name of one and the same object throughout the proof. Outside of the context of the proof, however, it is a variable. (For example, having proved some result concerning an

x which is divisible by 3, one feels free to apply it to all such numbers.) The reader is familiar with such names as "parameter" and "arbitrary constant" for symbols employed in this way.

This brings us to our basic definition. The formula B is a **valid consequence** of formulas $A_1, A_2, \cdots, A_m$ (in the predicate calculus), symbolized by

$$A_1, A_2, \cdots, A_m \vDash B,$$

iff for each domain D and for each assignment to the A's in D the formula B receives the value T whenever each A receives the value T. Further, if a variable x occurs free in any A, then in each assignment to the A's one chooses for all free occurrences of x one and the same value in D; that is, in making an assignment to the A's, such an x is regarded as a constant.

The statement and proof of Theorem 2.6 and its Corollary carry over unchanged to the present case. Thus, these results are available. In particular, to conclude that $A_1, A_2, \cdots, A_m \vDash B$, it is sufficient to prove that $\vDash A_1 \wedge A_2 \wedge \cdots \wedge A_n \rightarrow B$. Since Theorem 2.7 likewise extends to the predicate calculus, it is possible to give a demonstration that a formula B is a valid consequence of $A_1, A_2, \cdots, A_m$ in the form of a finite sequence of steps, the last of which is B. In addition to the two basic rules p and t, which in the statement calculus serve to justify the appearance of a formula E in a demonstration, we may introduce others for the predicate calculus. The most fundamental of these are the following two.

Rule (of universal specification) *us:* There is a formula $(x)A(x)$ preceding E such that E is $A(y)$, the result of substituting y for x in $A(x)$, such substitutions being restricted by the requirement that none of the resulting occurrences of y is bound.

Rule (of universal generalization) *ug:* E is of the form $(x)A(x)$ where $A(x)$ is a preceding formula such that x is not a variable having a free occurrence in any premise.

The state of affairs regarding a demonstration of valid consequence in the predicate calculus is then this. We contend that $A_1, A_2, \cdots, A_m \vDash B$ if we can devise a string

$$E_1, E_2, \cdots, E_r(=B)$$

of formulas such that the presence of each E can be accounted for on the basis of one of the rules *p*, *t*, *us*, or *ug*. Indeed, as in Section 2.4, it is possible to prove that if the presence of each *E* can be so justified, then

$$A_1, A_2, \cdots, A_m \vDash \quad \text{(any } E \text{ in the sequence).}$$

The earlier proof carries over (using the extended form of Theorem 2.7) to dispose of the case where the presence of an *E* is justified by either rule *p* or rule *t*. The cases which involve rule *us* or *ug* are dispatched using Theorem 2.10(I) and Theorem 2.11(I). The details are left as an exercise.

We are now in a position to construct formal derivations of simple arguments in the style developed in Section 2.4.

EXAMPLES

1. Consider the following argument.

> No human beings are quadrupeds. All women are human beings. Therefore, no women are quadrupeds.

Using the methods of translation of Section 2.6, we symbolize this as follows.

$$(x)(Hx \rightarrow \sim Qx)$$
$$(x)(Wx \rightarrow Hx)$$
$$\overline{(x)(Wx \rightarrow \sim Qx)}$$

The derivation proceeds as follows.

{1}	(1) $(x)(Hx \rightarrow \sim Qx)$	*p*
{2}	(2) $(x)(Wx \rightarrow Hx)$	*p*
{2}	(3) $Wy \rightarrow Hy$	2 *us*
{1}	(4) $Hy \rightarrow \sim Qy$	1 *us*
{1,2}	(5) $Wy \rightarrow \sim Qy$	3, 4 *t*
{1,2}	(6) $(x)(Wx \rightarrow \sim Qx)$	5 *ug*

2. The following argument is more involved.

> Everyone who buys a ticket receives a prize. Therefore, if there are no prizes, then nobody buys a ticket.

If *Bxy* is "*x* buys *y*," *Tx* is "*x* is a ticket," *Px* is "*x* is a prize," and *Rxy* is "*x* receives *y*," then the hypothesis and conclusion may be symbolized as follows.

$$(x)((\exists y)(Bxy \wedge Ty) \rightarrow (\exists y)(Py \wedge Rxy))$$
$$\sim(\exists x)Px \rightarrow (x)(y)(Bxy \rightarrow \sim Ty)$$

Since the conclusion is a conditional, we employ the rule *cp* in the derivation below. The deduction of line 3 from line 2, that of line 7 from line 6, and that of line 11 from 10 should be studied and justified by the reader.

{1}	(1)	$(x)((\exists y)(Bxy \wedge Ty) \rightarrow (\exists y)(Py \wedge Rxy))$	*p*
{2}	(2)	$\sim(\exists x)Px$	*p*
{2}	(3)	$(x)\sim Px$	2 *t*
{2}	(4)	$\sim Py$	3 *us*
{2}	(5)	$\sim Py \vee \sim Rxy$	4 *t*
{2}	(6)	$(y)(\sim Py \vee \sim Rxy)$	5 *ug*
{2}	(7)	$\sim(\exists y)(Py \wedge Rxy)$	6 *t*
{1}	(8)	$(\exists y)(Bxy \wedge Ty) \rightarrow (\exists y)(Py \wedge Rxy)$	1 *us*
{1,2}	(9)	$\sim(\exists y)(Bxy \wedge Ty)$	7, 8 *t*
{1,2}	(10)	$(y)(\sim Bxy \vee \sim Ty)$	9 *t*
{1,2}	(11)	$(y)(Bxy \rightarrow \sim Ty)$	10 *t*
{1,2}	(12)	$(x)(y)(Bxy \rightarrow \sim Ty)$	11 *ug*
{1}	(13)	$\sim(\exists x)Px \rightarrow (x)(y)(Bxy \rightarrow \sim Ty)$	2, 12 *cp*

3. Once the reader has subscribed to the soundness of the derivation in the preceding example, he has, in effect, endorsed further rules of inference which serve to expedite derivations. We introduce still two further derived rules of inference which render the same service. These are formal analogues of two familiar everyday occurrences in mathematics. If one is assured that "$(\exists x)P(x)$" is true, one feels at liberty to "choose" a *y* such that $P(y)$. Then *y* is an unknown fixed quantity such that *Py*. Conversely, given that there is some *y* such that *Py*, one does not hesitate to infer that "$(\exists x)P(x)$" is true. In the predicate calculus the rule which permits the passage from $(\exists x)P(x)$ to $P(y)$ is called the *rule* (of existential specification) *es*. The rule which permits the passage from $P(y)$ to $(\exists x)P(x)$ is called the *rule* (of existential generalization) *eg*. These are the analogues for existential quantifiers of the rules *us* and *ug* for universal quantifiers. We shall not validate these rules nor even discuss the restrictions which must be observed in using them. In the following simple example illustrating them we employ a lower-case Greek letter to designate an object which is involved in the "act of choice" accompanying an instance of the rule *es*.

Every member of the committee is wealthy and a Republican. Some committee members are old. Therefore, there are some old Republicans.

{1}	(1)	$(x)(Cx \rightarrow Wx \wedge Rx)$	p
{2}	(2)	$(\exists x)(Cx \wedge Ox)$	p
{2}	(3)	$C\alpha \wedge O\alpha$	2 *es*
{1}	(4)	$C\alpha \rightarrow W\alpha \wedge R\alpha$	1 *us*
{2}	(5)	$C\alpha$	3 *t*
{1,2}	(6)	$W\alpha \wedge R\alpha$	4, 5 *t*
{2}	(7)	$O\alpha$	3 *t*
{1,2}	(8)	$R\alpha$	6 *t*
{1,2}	(9)	$O\alpha \wedge R\alpha$	7, 8 *t*
{1,2}	(10)	$(\exists x)(Ox \wedge Rx)$	9 *eg*

4. The derivation corresponding to the following argument employs all of the rules which we have described.

> Some Republicans like all Democrats. No Republican likes any Socialist. Therefore, no Democrat is a Socialist.

The reason for the introduction of "x" in line 3 below is this. By virtue of the form of the conclusion, $(x)(Dx \rightarrow \sim Sx)$, a conditional proof is given. Thus, Dx is introduced as a premise in line 3. Since x occurs free here, we note its presence (as well as in subsequent lines which depend on this premise) to assist in avoiding any abuse of rule *ug*.

{1}	(1)	$(\exists x)(Rx \wedge (y)(Dy \rightarrow Lxy))$	p
{2}	(2)	$(x)(Rx \rightarrow (y)(Sy \rightarrow \sim Lxy))$	p
{3}	(3)	Dx	x, p
{1}	(4)	$R\alpha \wedge (y)(Dy \rightarrow L\alpha y)$	1 *es*
{1}	(5)	$(y)(Dy \rightarrow L\alpha y)$	4 *t*
{1}	(6)	$Dx \rightarrow L\alpha x$	5 *us*
{1,3}	(7)	$L\alpha x$	x, 3, 6 *t*
{2}	(8)	$R\alpha \rightarrow (y)(Sy \rightarrow \sim L\alpha y)$	2 *us*
{1}	(9)	$R\alpha$	4 *t*
{1,2}	(10)	$(y)(Sy \rightarrow \sim L\alpha y)$	8, 9 *t*
{1,2}	(11)	$Sx \rightarrow \sim L\alpha x$	10 *us*
{1,2,3}	(12)	$\sim Sx$	x, 7, 11 *t*
{1,2}	(13)	$Dx \rightarrow \sim Sx$	3, 12 *cp*
{1,2}	(14)	$(x)(Dx \rightarrow \sim Sx)$	13 *ug*

The foregoing examples lend plausibility to the contention that the predicate calculus is adequate for formalizing a wide variety of arguments. Lest there be concern over the lengths of derivations of such simple arguments as those considered, we assure the reader that an extended treatment would include the introduction of further derived rules of inference to streamline derivations. The outcome is the concept of an "informal proof." In mathematics this amounts to a derivation in the conversational style to which one is accustomed: mention of rules of inference and tautologies used is suppressed, and attention is drawn only to the mathematical (that is, nonlogical) axioms and earlier theorems employed. (Further details of this are supplied in the next chapter.) The principal advantage which accrues in having informal proofs as the evolution of formal derivations is this: One has a framework within which it can be decided in an objective and mechanical way, in case of disagreement, whether a purported proof is truly a proof.

EXERCISES

Construct a derivation corresponding to each of the following arguments.

1. No freshman likes any sophomore. All residents of Dascomb are sophomores. Therefore, no freshman likes any resident of Dascomb. (*Fx, Lxy, Sx, Dx*)

2. Art is a boy who does not own a car. Jane likes only boys who own cars. Therefore, Jane does not like Art. (*Bx, Ox, Lxy, a, j*)

3. No Republican or Democrat is a Socialist. Norman Thomas is a Socialist. Therefore, he is not a Republican. (*Rx, Dx, Sx, t*)

4. Every rational number is a real number. There is a rational number. Therefore, there is a real number.

5. All rational numbers are real numbers. Some rationals are integers. Therefore, some real numbers are integers. (*Qx, Rx, Zx*)

6. All freshmen date all sophomores. No freshman dates any junior. There are freshmen. Therefore, no sophomore is a junior.

7. No pusher is an addict. Some addicts are people with a record. Therefore, some people with a record are not pushers.

8. Some freshmen like all sophomores. No freshmen likes any junior. Therefore, no sophomore is a junior. (*Fx, Lxy, Sx, Jx*)

9. Some persons admire Elvis. Some persons like no one who admires Elvis. Therefore, some persons are not liked by all persons. (*Px, Ex, Lxy*)

Chapter 3

Axiomatic Theories

One of the striking aspects of twentieth century mathematical research is the enormously increased role which the axiomatic approach plays. The axiomatic method is certainly not new in mathematics, having been employed by Euclid in his *Elements*. However, only in relatively recent years has it been adopted in parts of mathematics other than geometry. This has become possible because of a fuller understanding of the nature of axioms and the axiomatic method. The first part of this chapter (Sections 3.1–3.4) treats the axiomatic method (by way of the notion of an informal axiomatic theory) to the extent it is used in everyday mathematics. An understanding of this part of the chapter is adequate preparation for the next chapter. The remainder of this chapter is an introductory discussion of axiomatic theories for which the first-order predicate calculus suffices as a logical base and in which this system of logic is explicitly incorporated. Thereby, various technical questions pertaining to axiomatic theories can be posed and discussed with precision.

3.1. The Concept of an Axiomatic Theory

The concept to be described is an outgrowth of the method used by Euclid to organize ancient Greek geometry. The plan of his *Elements* was as follows. It began with (what Euclid apparently regarded as satisfactory) definitions of certain *primitive terms*, such as *point*, *line*, and *plane*. Next appeared various properties (some of which were called *axioms* and the others *postulates*) of these primitive terms. Evidently, these properties were to be accepted as true on the basis of meaning suggested by the definitions of the terms involved. Further, other notions were defined in terms of the primitive ones, and other properties, called *theorems*, were deduced by logical means from the axioms and postulates. Since his geometry was intended to be a description of the actual physical space in which we live, it was only natural that Euclid assigned meaning to such terms as "point" and "line" and regarded his axioms as "self-evident truths." This attitude with respect to the nature of axioms still persists in the minds of many. Indeed, in current nonmathematical writings it is not uncommon to see such phrases as "It is axiomatic that" and "It is a fundamental postulate of" used to mean that some statement is beyond all logical opposition. Within mathematics this point of view with respect to the nature of axioms has altered radically. The change was gradual and it accompanied the full understanding of the discovery by J. Bolyai and (independently by) N. Lobachevsky of a non-Euclidean geometry. Let us elaborate on this matter.

In the traditional sense a non-Euclidean geometry is a geometry whose formulation coincides with that of Euclidean geometry with the one exception that Euclid's fifth postulate (the "parallel postulate") is denied. The fifth postulate is: "If two lines are cut by a third so as to make the sum of the two interior angles on one side less than two right angles, then the two lines, if produced, meet on that side on which the interior angle sum is less than two right angles." An equivalent formulation, in the sense that either, together with the remaining postulates, implies the other, and one which is better suited for comparison purposes, is: "In a plane, if point A is not on the line l, then there is exactly one line on A parallel to l." This is one of many axioms equivalent to the parallel postulate which were obtained as byproducts of unsuccessful attempts to substantiate the belief that the parallel postulate could be derived from Euclid's remaining axioms. Bolyai and Lobachevsky dispelled this belief by developing a geometry in which the parallel postulate was replaced by the statement, "In a plane, if the point A is not on line l, then there exists more than one line on A parallel to l." Apparently, the "truth" of this new geometry was initially in doubt. But on the basis of measurements that could be made in the portion of physical space available, there appeared to be no measurable differences between the predictions of the Bolyai–Lobachevsky geometry and those of Euclidean geometry. Also, each geometry, when studied as a deductive system, appeared to be consistent insofar as not yielding contradictory statements. The ability to examine these geometries from the latter point of view represented a great advance, for, in essence, it amounted to the detachment of physical meaning from the primitive terms of point, line, and so on.

A second advance in the attitude toward the axiomatic method accompanied the creation of various models in Euclidean geometry of the Bolyai–Lobachevsky geometry. A typical example is the model proposed in 1871 by Felix Klein, for which he interpreted the primitive terms of plane, point, and line, respectively, as the interior of a fixed circle in the Euclidean plane, a Euclidean point inside this circle, and an open-ended chord of this circle. If, in addition, distances and angles are computed by formulas developed by A. Cayley, in 1859, then all axioms of plane Bolyai–Lobachevsky geometry become true statements. The immediate value of such an interpretation was to establish the relative consistency (a concept which will be described in detail later) of the Bolyai–Lobachevsky geometry. That is, if Euclidean geometry is a consistent logical structure, then so is the Bolyai–Lobachevsky geometry. Of greater significance, insofar as understanding the nature of axiomatic theories, was the entertainment of the possibility of varying the meaning of the primitive terms of an axiomatic theory while holding fixed its deductive structure.

This evolution in the understanding of the nature of the axiomatic method set the stage for the present-day concept of an axiomatic theory. In its technical sense the word "theory" is applied to two sets of statements, of which one is a distinguished subset of the other. The entire set of statements defines the subject matter of the theory. The members of the distinguished subset are those statements which are classified as true, or provable. In the sciences, apart from mathematics, the distinguished statements are true statements about the real world, and the final appeal is to experiment. In an axiomatic theory the distinguished statements are called *provable statements*, or *theorems*, and are defined to be those statements of the theory which are deducible by logic alone from certain initially chosen statements called *axioms*. The notion of truth has no role whatsoever in an axiomatic theory proper; the truth of the statements is of concern only in possible applications. In any circumstance in which the axioms are accepted as true statements the theorems must be accepted as true statements (provided the system of logic is also accepted), since the theorems follow from the axioms by logic alone.

We elaborate on the foregoing to the extent of giving a precise definition of *theorem*. First, however, we define the notion of *proof*. A (**formal**) **proof** is a finite sequence $S_1, S_2, \cdots, S_k$ of statements of the theory such that each S either is an axiom or comes from one or more preceding S's by a logical rule of inference. A **theorem** or **provable statement** is a statement which is the last statement of some proof. Note that, in particular, an axiom is a theorem with a one-step proof.

We define next a generalization of the notion of a provable statement. Let Γ be a finite set of statements of an axiomatic theory. Then C is **deducible from** Γ, symbolized by

$$\Gamma \vdash C,$$

iff there is a finite sequence $S_1, S_2, \cdots, S_k$ of statements where S_k is C and each S is one of the following: an axiom, a statement in Γ, or a statement derived from one or more preceding S's by a rule of inference. The sequence $S_1, S_2, \cdots, S_k$ is called a **formal deduction** of C from Γ. The statements in Γ are called **assumptions.** In the special case where Γ is empty we write

$$\vdash C.$$

A deduction of C from no assumptions is simply a proof of C.

Often, axiomatic theories are the outgrowths of intuitive theories. One's first exposure to such subjects as arithmetic, mechanics, probability, and geometry is usually by way of an intuitive approach. After an intuitive theory has been advanced to the point where its basic properties are believed known, and reliable predictions can be made with it, an axiomatization can be attempted. The first step is to list

what are judged to be the basic objects discussed by the theory together with what are judged to be a set of fundamental properties
which are true of these objects. Then symbols (including, possibly,
words) are introduced as names for these objects, and the set of fundamental properties is rewritten in terms of this symbolism. The symbols
introduced are called the **primitive terms** (or, **symbols**) of the theory
under formulation, and the initial statements involving these are called
the **axioms** of the theory. Then, within the framework of a specified
system of logic, theorems are deduced. In order to meet one of the
requirements of an axiomatic theory—namely, that truth plays no
role—the primitive terms are taken to be undefined, and the axioms
are taken as simply an initial stock of theorems. A gage of one's degree
of success in axiomatizing an intuitive theory is the number of theorems
which, when the primitive terms appearing in them are assigned their
intuitive meaning, are true within one's knowledge. In such a program
of axiomatization of an intuitive theory there is usually considerable
leeway in the choice of the basic notions. Often, various combinations
are possible. For example, in the modern axiomatic treatment of
Euclidean geometry devised by D. Hilbert, the six primitive terms of
point, line, plane, incidence, betweeness, and congruence appear. On
the other hand, in the treatment devised by M. Pieri, there are but
two primitive terms: point and motion.

Another stimulus for the creation of axiomatic theories is the observation of basic likenesses in the central features of several different
theories. This may prompt an investigator to distill out these common
features and use them as a guide for defining an axiomatic theory in
the manner described above. Any one of the theories which an axiomatic theory is intended to formalize serves as a potential source of
definitions and possible theorems of this axiomatic theory. An axiomatic theory which successfully formalizes an intuitive theory is a
source of insight into the nature of that theory, since the axiomatic
theory is developed without reference to meaning. One which formalizes each of several theories to some degree has the additional merit
that it effects simplicity and efficiency. Since such an axiomatic theory
has an interpretation in each of its parent theories (on an assignment
of meaning to its primitive terms), it produces simplicity because it
tends to reduce the number of assumptions which have to be taken
into account for particular theorems in any one of the parent theories.

Efficiency is effected, because a theorem of the axiomatic theory yields a theorem of each of the parent theories. Herein lies one of the principal virtues of taking the primitive terms of an axiomatic theory as undefined.

A by-product of the creation of an axiomatic theory which is the common denominator of several theories is the possibility of enriching and extending given theories in an inexpensive way. For example, a theorem in one theory may be the origin of a theorem in the derived theory and it, in turn, may yield a new result in another parent theory. In addition to the possible enrichment in content of one theory by another, by way of an axiomatic theory derived from both, there is also the possibility of "cross-fertilization" insofar as methods of attack on problems are concerned. That is, a method of proof which is standard for one theory may provide a new method in another theory with a derived theory serving as the linkage.

A full understanding of such remarks as the foregoing cannot possibly be achieved until one has acquired some familiarity with a variety of specific theories and analyzed some successful attempts to bring diverse theories under a single heading. The field of algebra abounds in such successful undertakings. Indeed, it is perhaps in algebra that this type of genesis and exploitation of theories has scored its greatest successes. Several important examples of algebraic (axiomatic) theories are discussed later.

3.2. Informal Axiomatics

If in the presentation of an axiomatic theory the system of logic employed is presupposed as already known, we shall say that the theory is an **informal theory.** In mathematics it is standard practice to present axiomatic theories as informal theories. As to the system of logic which is thereby presupposed, usually it is the intuitive one which is acquired by studying mathematics! This statement is not quite as circular as it may seem. In Chapter 2 there is evidence that a system of logic which is adequate for much of mathematics can be described in precise terms (this is outlined later in this chapter). Further, there is considerable evidence to support the contention that the definition of logical correctness which is supplied by the symbolic logic which we have in mind is closely attuned to the corresponding intuitive notion which mathematicians acquire. Such a book as *Logic for Mathematicians*, by J. B. Rosser, is rich in examples which illustrate his thesis that logical principles which are judged correct by most mathematicians are classified as correct by symbolic logic and vice versa. We believe that it is accurate to assert that a vast majority of mathematicians accept modern symbolic logic as a formalization of the sort of intuitive reasoning to which they give approval. This does not evidence itself in mathematicians giving formal proofs and then using the mechanical procedures provided by the predicate calculus for testing the correctness of them. However, it does appear in their using mechanical checks at critical points in an involved argument and in their applying formal methods of reasoning to supplement intuitive methods in complex situations.

We proceed now to the description of several informal theories.

EXAMPLE A

Our first example of an informal theory is based on likenesses which one might observe in two familiar mathematical systems. The first system consists of the set $G(X)$ of all one-to-one mappings on a nonempty set X onto itself, together with function composition. The second system consists of the set Z of integers together with the familiar operation of addition. On the basis of results obtained in Chapter 1, and our knowledge of the number system, we may assert that: (i) each operation is a binary operation in the corresponding set; (ii) each operation is associative; (iii) in each set there is a distinguished element [namely, i_X in $G(X)$ and 0 in Z] such that when it is combined with any element of the set to which it belongs the same element results; and (iv) for each element of either set there exists an element of the same set such that when the two are combined the distinguished element of that set results [that is, $f \circ f^{-1} = f^{-1} \circ f = i_X$ and $x + (-x) = (-x) + x = 0$].

This similarity may be taken as the motivation for formulating the axiomatic theory known as **group theory.** As primitive terms we choose a (nonempty) set G, a binary operation, for which we shall use multiplicative notation (that is, the operation will be symbolized by $\cdot$), and an element e of G. The axioms are the following.

G_0.   For every a and b in G, the product $a \cdot b$ is a unique element of G.

G_1.　For all a, b, and c in G, $a \cdot (b \cdot c) = (a \cdot b) \cdot c$.

G_2.　For every a in G, $a \cdot e = e \cdot a = a$.

G_3.　For each a in G there exists an a' in G such that $a \cdot a' = a' \cdot a = e$.

The above is a description of the starting point of group theory as one might find it in an algebra text. An element which satisfies G_2 is called an **identity** element of G, and an element which satisfies G_3 for a given a is called an **inverse** of a (relative to e). The terminology "a binary operation" means simply a function f on $G \times G$. In terms of the symbol used for this function, its value at $\langle a,b \rangle$ is written $a \cdot b$ or simply ab. Then G_0 is the assumption that $ab \in G$, that is, that f is a binary operation in G (using terminology introduced in Chapter 1). As an alternative formulation we might specify that $\cdot$ be a binary operation in G (thereby incorporating G_0 implicitly) and then list G_1, G_2, and G_3 as axioms.

Several basic theorems of group theory are proved next.

G_4.　G contains exactly one identity element.

Proof. In view of G_2, only a proof of the uniqueness is required. Assume that each of e_1 and e_2 is an identity element of G. Then $e_1a = a$ for every a, and $ae_2 = a$ for every a. In particular, $e_1e_2 = e_2$ and $e_1e_2 = e_1$. Hence, $e_1 = e_2$ by G_0 and by properties of equality.

G_5.　Each element in G has exactly one inverse.

Proof. Since G_3 asserts the existence of an inverse for each element a, only the proof of its uniqueness remains. Assume that both a' and a'' are inverses of a. Then $a''a = e$ and $aa' = e$. By G_1, $(a''a)a' = a''(aa')$, and, hence, $ea' = a''e$. Using G_2 it follows that $a' = a''$.

In multiplicative notation the inverse of a is designated by a^{-1}; thus $a^{-1}a = aa^{-1} = e$ (the unique identity element of G).

G_6.　For every a, b, and c in G, if $ab = ac$, then $b = c$, and, if $ba = ca$, then $b = c$.

Proof. Assume that $ab = ac$. Now $a^{-1}(ab) = (a^{-1}a)b = eb = b$. On the other hand, $a^{-1}(ab) = a^{-1}(ac) = (a^{-1}a)c = ec = c$. Hence, $b = c$. The proof of the remaining assertion is similar.

Proofs of the next two theorems are left as exercises.

G_7.   For all a and b in G, each of the equations $ax = b$ and $ya = b$ has a unique solution in G.

G_8.   For all a and b in G, $(ab)^{-1} = b^{-1}a^{-1}$.

EXAMPLE B

The theory to be described has its origin in Euclidean plane geometry. It is that generalization of Euclidean geometry known as **affine geometry**. The primitive terms are a set $\mathcal{P}$ (whose members are called *points* and will be denoted by such letters as P, Q, $\cdots$), a set $\mathcal{L}$ (whose members are called *lines* and will be denoted by such letters as l, m, $\cdots$), and a set $\mathcal{J}$ called the *incidence relation*. The axioms are as follows.

AG_1. $\mathcal{J} \subseteq \mathcal{P} \times \mathcal{L}$. ($\langle P, l \rangle \in \mathcal{J}$ is read "P lies on l," or "l contains P," or "l passes through P").

AG_2.   For any two distinct points P and Q there is exactly one line passing through P and Q. (This line will be denoted by $P + Q$.)

AG_3.   For any point P and any line l there exists exactly one line m passing through P and *parallel* to l (that is, either $m = l$ or there exists no point which lies on both l and m).

AG_4.   If A, B, C, D, E, and F are six distinct points such that $A + B$ is parallel to $C + D$, $C + D$ is parallel to $E + F$, $A + C$ is parallel to $B + D$, and $C + E$ is parallel to $D + F$, then $A + E$ is parallel to $B + F$.

AG_5.   There exist three distinct points not on one line.

Proofs of a few simple theorems are called for in the following exercises.

EXAMPLE C

The theory which we introduce has its origin in properties of the sequence of natural numbers. Further, it may be taken as a basis for an axiomatization of the natural number system. The primitive terms are two sets, X and s, and the axioms are the following.

P_1. s is a function on X into X.

P_2. $X - s[X] \neq \varnothing$.

P_3. s is one-to-one.

P_4.   If $Y \subseteq X$, $s[Y] \subseteq Y$, and $Y \cap (X - s[X]) \neq \varnothing$, then $Y = X$.

These are essentially the celebrated *Peano axioms* for the natural number system. This theory was developed by the Italian mathematician and logician, G. Peano, in a book which appeared in 1889. The axioms themselves were devised by the German mathematician, R. Dedekind, in 1888.

Since axiomatic theories are often elaborate structures, they are deserving of elaborate symbols as names. To our mind, capital German letters meet the challenge. Suppose then that $\mathfrak{T}$ is an informal theory. An assignment of meaning to the primitive terms of $\mathfrak{T}$ is called an **interpretation** of $\mathfrak{T}$. If the entity made up of the meaningful versions of the primitive terms of $\mathfrak{T}$, as specified by an interpretation of $\mathfrak{T}$, satisfies the axioms of $\mathfrak{T}$, it is called a **model** of $\mathfrak{T}$. In terms of functions, the two definitions can be put as follows: An interpretation of $\mathfrak{T}$ is simply a function having as domain the set T of primitive terms of $\mathfrak{T}$. If $f[T]$ satisfies the axioms of $\mathfrak{T}$, then it is a model of $\mathfrak{T}$. Returning to Example A, the set $G(X)$, together with function composition, is a model of the theory of groups or, more simply, is a group. Again, $\underline{Z}$ with addition is a group (having 0 as the identity element and $-a$ as the inverse of a). Further, $\underline{R}^+$, together with ordinary multiplication, is a group. Finally, the power set of a nonempty set, together with symmetric difference as the operation and $\varnothing$, is a group.

Turning to Example B, one who is familiar, to some degree, with Euclidean geometry will undoubtedly accept it as an affine geometry. A radically different model results on setting $\mathcal{P} = \{1,2,3,4\}$, $\mathcal{L} = \{\{1,2\}, \{1,3\}, \{1,4\}, \{2,3\}, \{2,4\}, \{3,4\}\}$ and defining P to lie on l iff $P \in l$. The verification that all axioms are satisfied is left as an exercise.

In Example C, if X is interpreted as the set $\underline{N} = \{0, 1, 2, \cdots\}$ of natural numbers and s is interpreted as the successor function [that is, $s(x) = x + 1$], then the axioms express familiar properties of the natural number sequence. Since $\underline{N} - s[\underline{N}] = \{0\}$, axiom P_4 may be restated in the following simpler form: If M is a set of natural numbers such that $0 \in M$, and $k + 1 \in M$ whenever $k \in M$, then $M = \underline{N}$. This is the principle of induction for $\underline{N}$. Another model of this theory results on choosing X to be the sequence $\{a, ar, \cdots, ar^n, \cdots\}$ (where a and r are nonzero real numbers) and choosing s to be the function such that $s(ar^n) = ar^{n+1}$.

In terms of the notion of a model, one fact which was stressed in the preceding section may be stated in the following form: If $\mathfrak{M}$ is a model of an axiomatic theory $\mathfrak{T}$, then each theorem of $\mathfrak{T}$ yields a theorem of $\mathfrak{M}$ on assigning to each primitive term in $\mathfrak{T}$ its value in accordance with the interpretation at hand. This may be illustrated by Theorem G_8 in Example A. Taking G to be $G(X)$ and the operation to be function composition, G_8 yields the result that for all functions f and g in $G(X)$, $(g \circ f)^{-1} = f^{-1} \circ g^{-1}$. This is an important special case of the result appearing above Example B in Section 1.9. Again, taking G to be $\mathbf{Z}$ and the operation to be addition, G_8 yields the result that $-(a + b) = (-b) + (-a)$. Thus, these two results, diverse in appearance, are instances of one and the same general result.

EXERCISES

1. Prove Theorems G_7 and G_8 in Example A.

2. The theory of commutative groups differs from the theory of groups in that it includes one further axiom:

G_9.   For all a and b in G, $ab = ba$.

It is common practice to use additive notation for the operation in a commutative group (that is, to write $a + b$ instead of ab), to write 0 instead of e, and to write $-a$ instead of a^{-1}.

Suppose that G together with $+$ and 0 is a commutative group. Prove each of the following theorems.

(a) $-(a + b) = (-a) + (-b)$.

(b)   If "$a - b$" is an abbreviation for "$a + (-b)$," then $a + b = c$ iff $b = c - a$.

(c) $a - (-b) = a + b$ and $-(a - b) = b - a$.

(d)   If $f: G \rightarrow G$ where $f(a) = -a$, then f is a one-to-one and onto mapping.

3. Let $\mathbf{Z}_n$ be the set of residue classes $[a]$ of $\mathbf{Z}$ modulo n (see Section 1.7). Show that the relation $\{\langle\langle[a],\ [b]\rangle,\ [a + b]\rangle | [a],\ [b] \in \mathbf{Z}_n\}$ is a binary operation in $\mathbf{Z}_n$. Show that $\mathbf{Z}_n$ together with this operation and $[0]$ is a commutative group.

4. Show that an operation $+$ can be introduced in the set I of equivalence classes defined in Exercise 11, Section 1.7 by the definition $[a,b] + [c,d] = [a + c,\ b + d]$, where $[a,b]$ is the equivalence class

determined by $\langle a,b \rangle$, and so on. Prove that I together with this operation and $[1,1]$ is a commutative group.

5. Show that $\underline{R}$ together with the operation $\star$ such that x $\star$ y $= (x^3 + y^3)^{1/3}$ and 0 is a group.

6. Write out the elements of $G(X)$ for $X = \{1,2\}$ and for $X = \{1,2,3\}$. Show that the group associated with the latter set of mappings is not commutative.

7. Suppose that G is a nonempty set, that $\cdot$ is a binary operation in G, and that G_1 and G_7 hold. Prove that G with $\cdot$ is a group.

8. Suppose that G is a nonempty finite set, that $\cdot$ is a binary operation in G, and that G_1 and G_6 hold. Prove that G with $\cdot$ is a group.

9. This exercise is concerned with affine geometry as formulated in the text.

(a) Prove that "is parallel to" is an equivalence relation on $\mathfrak{L}$. An equivalence class is called a *pencil* of lines.

(b) Let L_1 and L_2 be two pencils of lines. Using only AG_2 and Ag_3, establish a one-to-one correspondence between the points contained in a line l of L_1 and the lines of L_2.

(c) Using (b), deduce that if there exist three distinct pencils of parallel lines, then there exists a one-to-one correspondence between the lines of any two pencils and between the points of any two lines.

(d) From AG_5 infer that there exist at least three distinct pencils of lines.

(e) Show that the set of four points and six lines given in the text is a model of the theory.

(f) Show that any affine geometry contains at least four points and six lines.

10. Let $\mathfrak{S}$ be the axiomatic theory having as its primitive terms two sets P and L and as its axioms the following.

A_1.   If $l \in L$, then $l \subseteq P$.

A_2.   If a and b are distinct elements of P, then there exists exactly one member l of L such that $a, b \in l$.

A_3.   For every l in L there is exactly one l' in L such that l and l' are disjoint.

A_4. L is nonempty.

A_5.   Every member of L is finite and nonempty.

Establish the following theorems for $\mathfrak{S}$.

(a) Each member of L contains at least two elements.
(b) P contains at least four elements.
(c) L contains at least six elements.
(d) Each member of L contains exactly two elements.

3.3. Informal Theories Within the Context of Set Theory

There is one questionable feature of the foregoing discussion of informal theories. On one hand we have emphasized that the primitive terms of a theory are unspecified (apart from those properties required by the axioms of the theory), whereas on the other hand the primitive terms have been *sets* in each of the examples considered. That is, the general character of the primitive terms has been specified. There are ways to remedy this inconsistency, one of which we shall now discuss.

Our approach calls for an axiomatization of set theory as the first step and then *definitions* of the theories we have discussed by way of set-theoretical predicates. We shall not present an axiomatization of set theory here; instead, we merely assure the reader that this can be done in such a way that (i) insofar as is known, all undesirable features (for example, the Russell paradox) are avoided, and (ii) all desirable features, consonant with (i), are retained. Suppose, then, that such an informal theory of sets is available for use. Now we make a general observation (which is substantiated, in part, by those theories discussed in Examples A, B, and C of the preceding section). The primitive terms of a great variety of mathematical theories consist of a set X and certain *constants* associated with X. These constants may be of various types: elements of X (such as the identity element of a group), subsets of X, families of subsets of X (such as the lines of an affine geometry), subsets of X^n for some n (which include relations in X and operations in X), and so on. Collectively, the constants serve as the basis for imposing a certain structure on X (which is the object of study of the theory). The structure itself is given in the axioms, which are the assumptions made about X and the constants (including, possibly, the existence of interrelations among them). In brief, a theory of sets which has the breadth of intuitive set theory is sufficiently rich in expressive powers to enable us to define a great variety of mathematical theories.

We shall consider two examples of definitions of mathematical theories within the context of a theory of sets. The first is that of the theory of partially ordered sets. The purely set-theoretical character of the predicate "is a partially ordered set" which is defined next should be apparent.

DEFINITION A. $\mathfrak{A}$ is a partially ordered set iff it is an ordered pair $\langle X, \rho \rangle$ such that X is a set, ρ is a binary relation, and

O_1. ρ is reflexive in X;
O_2. ρ is antisymmetric in X;
O_3. ρ is transitive in X.

This definition illustrates the convention which we shall follow of exhibiting the basic set as the first coordinate of an ordered n-tuple, and the associated constants, in some order, as the remaining coordinates.

An alternative to Definition A, which is closer to standard mathematical practice, is a conditional definition.

DEFINITION B. Let X be a set and ρ be a binary relation. Then $\langle X, \rho \rangle$ is a partially ordered set iff

O_1. ρ is reflexive in X;
O_2. ρ is antisymmetric in X;
O_3. ρ is transitive in X.

This definition is conditional in the sense that the proper definition is prefaced by a hypothesis. When a definition is so formulated it is common practice to omit the hypothesis in stating theorems of the theory.

Our second example is a definition of group theory along the lines suggested by the axiomatization appearing in Example A of the preceding section.

DEFINITION C. $\mathfrak{G}$ is a group iff it is an ordered triple $\langle X, \cdot, e \rangle$ such that X is a set, $\cdot$ is a binary operation in X, e is a member of X, and

G_1.   for all a, b, and c in X, $a \cdot (b \cdot c) = (a \cdot b) \cdot c$;
G_2.   for all a in X, $a \cdot e = e \cdot a = a$;
G_3.   for each a in X there exists an a' in X such that $a \cdot a' = a' \cdot a = e$.

It is not uncommon to find as an alternative to this definition something such as the following.

DEFINITION D.   A set X is a group with respect to the binary operation $\cdot$ iff $\cdots$.

The predicate here is so lengthy that it is usually agreed to refer to the set X alone as a group. This is incorrect, but tradition lends its weight to the convention.

We conclude this section with several remarks. First, when a mathematical theory is presented within set theory the statements which were originally called the axioms of the theory appear as ingredients of the definition of that theory. Further, the term "primitive term" is no longer appropriate, since under the circumstances the only primitive terms at hand are those of set theory. However, it is common practice (one to which we adhere) to ignore this observation. Again, we note that when a theory is defined within set theory, theorems of the theory take the form of conditional statements. For example, a theorem of group theory is stated as "If G is a group, then $\cdots$." Finally, we observe that if a theory $\mathfrak{T}$ is defined by a set-theoretical predicate, then models of $\mathfrak{T}$ are simply those entities which satisfy the predicate. For the theory of groups, for example, the point can be put quite trivially as follows: If $\langle X, \cdot, e \rangle$ is a group, then $\langle X, \cdot, e \rangle$ is a model for the theory of groups.

EXERCISES

These exercises are concerned with the theory of simply ordered commutative groups, which may be defined as follows: $\mathfrak{G}$ is a simply ordered commutative group (*s.o.c.g.*) iff $\mathfrak{G} = \langle G, +, 0, \leq \rangle$, where

SG$_1$. $\langle G, +, 0 \rangle$ is a commutative group;

SG$_2$. $\langle G, \leq \rangle$ is a simply ordered set;

SG$_3$.   for all a, b, and c in G, if $a < b$, then $a + c < b + c$. (Here, "$a < b$" is an abbreviation for "$a \leq b$ and $a \neq b$.")

All results obtained earlier for groups, in particular, commutative groups, may be used when needed. Also, properties of simply ordered sets, may be used.

1. Find two *s.o.c.g.* within the real number system.

    2. If $\langle G,+,0,\leq,\rangle$ is a *s.o.c.g.*, define G^+ to be $\{a \in G | 0 < a\}$. Prove the following properties of G^+.

    (a) If $a \in G^+$, then $-a \notin G^+$.
    (b) If $a \neq 0$, then either $a \in G^+$ or $-a \in G^+$.
    (c) If, a, $b \in G^+$, then $a + b \in G^+$.

    3. Prove the following theorems for a *s.o.c.g.*

    (a) If $a < b$, then $a - c < b - c$.
    (b) If $a + c < b + c$, then $a < b$.
    (c) If $a < b$ and $c < d$, then $a + c < b + d$.
    (d) If $a < b$, then $-b < -a$.

    4. Prove the following theorem. If G has more than one element and $\langle G,+,0,\leq \rangle$ is a *s.o.c.g.*, then G has infinitely many elements.

3.4. Further Features of Informal Theories

    In this section we introduce a variety of notions which have relevance to informal theories. Most of these serve to provide a classification scheme for a given theory. Thereby its status and its merits can be summarized concisely.

    Suppose that S is a statement of some theory $\mathfrak{T}$ such that both S and $\sim S$ are theorems. Then, if the system of logic employed includes the statement calculus with modus ponens as a rule of inference, any statement T of the theory is a theorem. Indeed, $S \rightarrow (\sim S \rightarrow T)$ is a theorem since it is a tautology, and two uses of modus ponens establish T as a theorem. A theory $\mathfrak{T}$ is called **inconsistent** if it contains a statement S such that both S and $\sim S$ are theorems. A theory is called **consistent** if it is not inconsistent, that is, if it contains no statement S such that both S and $\sim S$ are theorems.

    Since in any theory which we shall consider the logical apparatus will include what was used above, we regard an inconsistent theory as worthless, since every statement is a theorem. Thus, the question of establishing the consistency of a theory becomes of primary importance. For informal (axiomatic) theories, the notion of a model suggests a means to cope with this. Indeed, if a theory is inconsistent, then every model of it contains a contradiction, since a pair of contradictory theorems translates into two contradictory statements of the model. Hence, a theory is consistent if there can be exhibited a model which is free of contradiction. Whenever a model of some theory $\langle X, \cdots \rangle$ can be found such that the interpretation of X is a *finite* set, one may expect that the question of whether it is free of contradiction can be settled by direct observation. For example, the fact that the unit set of an object e, together with the operation such that $e \cdot e = e$ is a model of group theory, establishes the consistency of group theory beyond all doubt.

In other cases, however, judging the consistency of a model (that is, its freedom from contradictions) may lead to complicated chains of reasoning which are not above suspicion. This could prove to be the case if, for example, a theory has only infinite models (that is, models where the interpretations of the basic set are infinite). Thus, in many cases attempts to establish the consistency of a theory by way of a model are merely relative in nature: if the model is consistent, then the theory is consistent. Let us consider some examples. As described in Section 3.1, an interpretation of the Bolyai–Lobachevsky geometry can be given in Euclidean geometry. Thereby the relative consistency of this non-Euclidean geometry is established in the form: If Euclidean geometry is consistent, then so is the Bolyai–Lobachevsky geometry. The consistency of Euclidean geometry (a precise formulation of which was given in 1899 by the German mathematician Hilbert in his book *Grundlagen der Geometrie*) has never been proved, although almost everyone "believes" it is consistent. A proof of its relative consistency can be given wherein a point is interpreted as an ordered pair of real numbers, and a line is interpreted as a relation defined by a linear equation; of course, in more familiar guise this is simply the standard coordinatization of the Euclidean plane. However, since the real number system has never been proved consistent one may conclude merely that if the real number system is consistent, then so is Euclidean geometry. In this and in other ways the consistency of large parts of classical mathematics is ultimately reducible to that of the arithmetic of natural numbers, as, for example, this theory is embodied in the Peano axioms or in a set theory sufficiently rich for the derivation of the Peano axioms.

Assuming that the consistency of a theory has been settled in the affirmative by proof or by faith, the question of its *completeness* may be raised. A theory is **complete** if it has enough theorems for some purpose. The variety of purposes which may enter in this connection is responsi-

ble for a variety of technical meanings being assigned to this notion.
We shall consider only the following: A theory $\mathfrak{T}$ is **complete** iff for
every statement S of $\mathfrak{T}$, either S or $\sim S$ is a theorem. This definition is
motivated by the fact that any statement S of $\mathfrak{T}$, when interpreted in a
model, is either true or false. Hence, one of S and $\sim S$ is true and
should be a theorem in $\mathfrak{T}$. A theory which is both consistent and complete possesses maximum consistency in the sense that the addition,
as an axiom, of any statement of the theory which is not a theorem
yields an inconsistent theory. The problem of completeness can best be
considered in connection with axiomatic theories in which the theory
of inference employed is explicitly incorporated into the theory. Such
theories are considered in the next section. For the present let it suffice
to say that the combination of consistency and completeness appears
to be unattainable for many important mathematical theories.

The foregoing remark regarding completeness applies equally well
to a discussion of the next notion pertaining to axiomatic theories.
This notion is related to the purpose for which a theory is devised. If
it is intended that an axiomatic theory formalize some one intuitive
theory, a measure of the successfulness of the axiomatization is whether
any two models are indistinguishable, apart from terminology and
notation. If such is the case, the primitive terms and axioms may be
regarded as constituting a complete set of key principles of the intuitive
theory. This type of indescernibility of two models is known as
isomorphism. A precise definition which could cover all conceivable
situations would be too unwieldy to attempt, which is the reason for
the repeated occurrence of definitions bearing this name—each is
tailored to fit the distinguishing features of the theory under consideration. We shall content ourselves by giving precise definitions in three
specific cases (labeled I_1, I_2, and I_3) and leave it to the reader to
extrapolate to more complex situations.

I_1.   Let $\langle X_1, \rho_1 \rangle$ and $\langle X_2, \rho_2 \rangle$ be two models of a theory having a set
and a pertinent relation as primitive terms. Then $\langle X_1, \rho_1 \rangle$ is isomorphic
to $\langle X_2, \rho_2 \rangle$ iff there exists a function f such that

   (i) f is a one-to-one correspondence between X_1 and X_2,

   (ii) if $x, y \in X_1$ and $x \, \rho_1 \, y$, then $f(x) \, \rho_2 \, f(y)$,

   (iii) if $x, y \in X_2$ and $x \, \rho_2 \, y$, then $f^{-1}(x) \, \rho_1 \, f^{-1}(y)$.

This definition is patterned after that of isomorphism for partially
ordered sets (Section 1.10). It is applicable to the case where ρ_i is a

function on X_i into X_i, $i = 1,2$. In this event the definition of isomorphism can be simplified to the following, as the reader can verify.

Let $\langle X_1, f_1 \rangle$ and $\langle X_2, f_2 \rangle$ be models of a theory whose primitive terms are a set and a function on that set into itself. Then $\langle X_1, f_1 \rangle$ is isomorphic to $\langle X_2, f_2 \rangle$ iff there exists a function f such that

   (i) f is a one-to-one correspondence between X_1 and X_2,

   (ii) if $x \in X_1$, then $f(f_1(x)) = f_2(f(x))$.

Thus, in this case only one of the two requirements for isomorphism must be proved; the other, which completes the symmetry inherent in the concept of isomorphism, necessarily follows.

I_2.   Let $\langle X_1, \circ_1 \rangle$ and $\langle X_2, \circ_2 \rangle$ be two models of a theory having a set and a binary operation in that set as its primitive terms. Then $\langle X_1, \circ_1 \rangle$ is isomorphic to $\langle X_2, \circ_2 \rangle$ iff there exists a function f such that

   (i) f is a one-to-one correspondence between X_1 and X_2,

   (ii) if $x, y \in X_1$, then $f(x \circ_1 y) = f(x) \circ_2 f(y)$.

It is left as an exercise to show that this formulation of isomorphism is an equivalence relation in any collection of models of the theory described. In particular, therefore, as in the specialized version of I_1 given above, the symmetric nature of the concept follows automatically.

I_3.   Let $\langle X_1, Y_1, \rho_1 \rangle$ and $\langle X_2, Y_2, \rho_2 \rangle$ be two models of a theory having as its primitive terms two sets and a relation whose domain is the first set and whose range is the second set. Then $\langle X_1, Y_1, \rho_1 \rangle$ is isomorphic to $\langle X_2, Y_2, \rho_2 \rangle$ iff there exists a function f such that

   (i) f is a one-to-one correspondence between $X_1 \cup Y_1$ and $X_2 \cup Y_2$ such that $f(X_1) = X_2$ and $f(Y_1) = Y_2$,

   (ii) f preserves the relations ρ_1 and ρ_2 in the sense of definition I_1.

This is not the only definition of isomorphism which might be made under the circumstances. The one given takes into account the preservation of set-theoretical interconnections between X_i and Y_i, $i = 1,2$.

An axiomatic theory is **categorical** iff any two models of it are isomorphic. That is, a categorical theory is focused on essentially one model. This, as we said earlier, is precisely the state of affairs one wishes to achieve if his goal is to axiomatize some one intuitive theory such as Euclidean geometry or the real number system. An elementary example of a categorical theory is obtained by adding to the five axioms for affine geometry (Example B, Section 3.2) the following:

   AG_6.   The set $\mathcal{P}$ has exactly four members.

The resulting theory is consistent by virtue of the model given after Example C, Section 3.2. The proof that this theory is categorical is left as an exercise.

A noncategorical, consistent theory has essentially different (that is, nonisomorphic) models. This is precisely what should be anticipated for a theory intended to axiomatize the common part of several different theories. The theory of groups is an excellent example. Because it has such a general character, it has a wide variety of models, which means that it has a wide range of application.

We conclude this section with several miscellaneous remarks. The first involves assigning a precise meaning to the word "formulation" which we have used frequently. As we described it, an informal theory $\mathfrak{T}$ includes a list T_0 of undefined terms, a list T_1 of defined terms, a list P_0 of axioms, and a list P_1 of all those other statements which can be inferred from P_0 in accordance with some system of logic. The set T_0 serves to generate $T_0 \cup T_1$, the set of all technical terms of $\mathfrak{T}$; the set P_0 serves to generate $P_0 \cup P_1$, the set of all theorems of $\mathfrak{T}$. For the ordered pair $\langle T_0, P_0 \rangle$ we propose the name of a "formulation" for $\mathfrak{T}$. A study of $\mathfrak{T}$ may very well culminate in the discovery of other useful formulations. To obtain one amounts to the determination of: (i) a set T_0' which is a subset of $T_0 \cup T_1$ (which may or may not differ from T_0), and (ii) a subset P_0' of $P_0 \cup P_1$ whose member statements are expressed in terms of the members of T_0' and from which the remaining theorems of the theory can be derived. For a pair of the form $\langle T_0', P_0' \rangle$ to be a formulation of $\mathfrak{T}$, it is clearly sufficient that the terms of T_0 can be defined by means of those in T_0' and that the statements of P_0 can be derived from those of P_0'. For many of the well-known axiomatic theories there exists a variety of formulations. This is true, for example, of the theory of Boolean algebras discussed in Chapter 4. A rather trivial example appears in Section 1.10, and we may rephrase it to suit our present purposes: As a different formulation of the theory of partially ordered sets we may take that consisting of a set X together with a relation that is irreflexive and transitive on X (see Exercise 3, Section 1.10). Another example is implicit in a remark made in Section 3.1; rephrased, it amounts to the assertion that Hilbert and Pieri gave different formulations of a theory which axiomatizes intuitive plane geometry.

Different formulations of a theory amount to one variety of possible approaches which can be made to one and the same mathematical structure. Depending on the criteria adopted, one may show a marked preference for one formulation over others. Aesthetic considerations may influence one's judgment, and the simplicity of the set of axioms in conjunction with the elegance of the proofs may also play an important role. One may prefer a particular formulation because he feels it has a "naturalness" that others lack. He may favor a formulation which involves the fewest number of primitive terms or axioms.

A notion which is pertinent to a formulation of an informal theory is that of the independence of the set of axioms. A set of axioms is **independent** if the omission of any one of them causes the loss of a theorem; otherwise it is **dependent**. A particular axiom (considered as a member of the set of axioms of some formulation) is **independent** if its omission causes the loss of a theorem; otherwise it is **dependent**. Clearly, an independent axiom cannot be proved from the others of a set of which it is a member. Further, the set of axioms of a formulation is independent iff each of its members is independent. Models may be used to establish the independence of axioms. For example, the independence of the axioms O_1, O_2, O_3 for the theory of partially ordered sets (see Section 3.3) may be shown by constructing a model of each of the three theories having exactly two of O_1, O_2, and O_3 as axioms and in which the interpretation of the missing axiom is false. The independence of a set of axioms is a matter of elegance. A dependent set simply contains one or more redundencies; this has no effect on the theory involved.

In order to motivate the final remark we recall Theorem 1.7, which asserts that every partially ordered set is isomorphic to a collection of sets partially ordered by inclusion. That is, to within isomorphism, all models of the theory of partially ordered sets are furnished by collections of sets. In general, a theorem to the effect that for a given axiomatic theory $\mathfrak{T}$ a distinguished subset of the set of all models has the property that every model is isomorphic to some member of this subset is a **representation theorem** for $\mathfrak{T}$. Analagous to the case of the theory of partially ordered sets where, from the outset, collections of sets constitute distinguished models, in the case of an arbitrary theory $\mathfrak{T}$, even though it is noncategorical, one particular type of model may seem more natural. In this event a **representation problem** arises—

the question whether there can be proved a representation theorem for $\mathfrak{T}$ which asserts that this type of model yields all models to within isomorphism. When such a problem is answered in the affirmative, new theorems may follow for $\mathfrak{T}$ by imitating proof techniques that have proved useful in those theories which, in effect, supply all models.

EXERCISES

1. (a) Establish the consistency of the theory of partially ordered sets by way of a model.
   (b) Show that this is a noncategorical theory.
   (c) Show that the set of axioms $\{O_1, O_2, O_3\}$ for partially ordered sets is independent.

2. (a) Show that the theory of groups is noncategorical.
   (b) Defining a group as an ordered triple $\langle G, \cdot, e \rangle$ such that G_1, G_2, and G_3 of Example A, Section 3.2 hold, establish the independence of $\{G_1, G_2, G_3\}$. (Suggestion: Use a multiplication table for displaying the operation which you introduce into any set.)

3. Consider the axiomatic theory having as its primitive terms two sets A and $\mathfrak{B}$ and having as axioms the following.

   (i) Each element of $\mathfrak{B}$ is a two-element subset of A.
   (ii) If a, a' is a pair of distinct elements of A, then $\{a, a'\} \in \mathfrak{B}$.
   (iii) $A \notin \mathfrak{B}$.
   (iv) If B, B' is a pair of distinct elements of $\mathfrak{B}$, then $B \cap B' \subseteq A$.

Show that this theory is consistent. Is it categorical?

4. Consider the axiomatic theory whose primitive terms are a nonempty A and a binary operation $\langle x, y \rangle \rightarrow x - y$ (that is, we write the image of $\langle x, y \rangle$ as $x - y$) in A, which satisfies the identity

$$y = x - [(x - z) - (y - z)].$$

Show that this theory is consistent.

5. Consider the axiomatic theory whose primitive terms are a nonempty set A, a binary operation $\langle x, y \rangle \rightarrow x \times y$ in A and a unary operation $x \rightarrow x'$ in A. The axioms are the following.

   (i) $\times$ is an associative operation.
   (ii) $(x \times y)' = y' \times x'$.
   (iii) If $x \times y = z \times z'$ for some z, then $x = y'$.
   (iv) If $x = y'$, then $x \times y = z \times z'$ for all z.

  (a) Show that the theory is consistent.

  (b) Show that this set of axioms is dependent.

  6. Prove the assertion made in the text to the effect that if ρ_i is a function on X_i into X_i, $i = 1,2$, then $\langle X_1, \rho_1 \rangle$ is isomorphic to $\langle X_2, \rho_2 \rangle$, provided there exists a one-to-one correspondence $f: X_1 \to X_2$ such that $f(\rho_1(x)) = \rho_2(f(x))$ for all x in X_1.

  7. Prove that the type of isomorphism labeled I_2 is an equivalence relation in any set whose members are systems consisting of a set together with an operation in that set.

  8. Assume that of two isomorphic models of the theory considered in Exercise 4, one is a group. Prove that the other is a group.

  9. The set $\{e,a,b,c\}$ together with the operation defined by the following multiplication table is a group. Determine six isomorphisms of this group with itself.

	e	a	b	c
e	e	a	b	c
a	a	e	c	b
b	b	c	e	a
c	c	b	a	e

  10. Devise a definition of isomorphism for systems consisting of a set together with two operations.

  11. Consider an axiomatic theory $\mathfrak{T}$ formulated in terms of two sets, whose members are called *points* and *lines*, respectively, and whose axioms are as follows.

  (i) Each line is a nonempty set of points.

  (ii) The intersection of two lines is a point.

  (iii) Each point is a member of exactly two lines.

  (iv) There are exactly four lines.

  (a) Show that $\mathfrak{T}$ is a consistent theory.

  (b) Show that there are exactly six points in a model of $\mathfrak{T}$.

  (c) Show that each line consists of exactly three points.

  (d) Find two models of $\mathfrak{T}$.

  (e) Is $\mathfrak{T}$ categorical? Give reasons for your answer.

  12. Show that the axiomatic theory defined in Exercise 4 is a formulation of the theory of commutative groups.

13. Show that the axiomatic theory defined in Exercise 5 is a formulation of the theory of groups.

14. Show that the following is another formulation of the theory of groups. A *group* is an ordered triple $\langle G, \cdot, ' \rangle$ such that G is a set, $\cdot$ is a binary operation in G, $'$ is a unary operation in G, and

(i) G is nonempty;
(ii) $\cdot$ is associative;
(iii) $a'(ab) = b = (ba)a'$ for all a and b.

15. Show that the following is another formulation of the theory of groups. A group is an ordered triple $\langle G, \cdot, e \rangle$ such that G is a set, $\cdot$ is a binary operation in G, e is a member of G, and

(i) $\cdot$ is an associative operation;
(ii) for each a in G, $ea = a$, and there exists a' in G such that $a'a = e$.

16. Consider the theory whose primitive terms are a set X, a binary operation $\cdot$ in X, and whose axioms are the following.

(i) X is nonempty.
(ii) $\cdot$ is an associative operation.
(iii) To each element a in X there corresponds an element e of X such that $ea = ae = a$, and a possesses an inverse a' relative to e in X (that is, $aa' = a'a = e$).

Show that if $\langle S, \cdot \rangle$ is a model of the theory, then there exists a partition of S such that each member set determines a group.

17. Consider the theory $\mathfrak{T}$ whose primitive terms are the power set of a set S and a mapping f on $\mathcal{P}(S)$ into itself, and whose axioms are as follows:

(i) For all X in $\mathcal{P}(S)$, $X^f \supseteq X$.
(ii) For all X in $\mathcal{P}(S)$, $(X^f)^f = X^f$.
(iii) For all X and Y in $\mathcal{P}(S)$, $X \supseteq Y$ implies $X^f \supseteq Y^f$.

Show that another formulation of $\mathfrak{T}$ results on adopting as the sole axiom:

$$(X \cup Y)^f \supseteq (X^f)^f \cup Y^f \cup Y, \text{ for all } X \text{ and } Y \text{ in } \mathcal{P}(S).$$

3.5. Formal Axiomatic Theories

In order to achieve precision in the presentation of a mathematical theory, symbols are used extensively. A formal theory carries symbolization to the ultimate in that all words are suppressed in favor of symbols. Moreover, in a formal theory the symbols are taken to be merely marks which are to be manipulated according to given rules which depend only on the form of the expressions composed from the symbols. Thus, in contrast to the usual usage of symbols in mathematics, symbols in a formal theory do not stand for objects. One further distinguishing feature of a formal theory is the fact that the system of logic employed is explicitly incorporated into the theory.

We require additional properties of the formal theories which we shall discuss. These involve an auxiliary notion which we dispose of first. In nontechnical terms, an **effective procedure** is a set of instructions that provides a mechanical procedure by which the answer to any one of a class of questions can be obtained in a finite number of steps. An effective procedure is like a recipe in that it tells what to do at each step and no intelligence is required to follow it. In principle, it is always possible to construct a machine for the purpose of carrying out such instructions.

The formal theories with which we shall be concerned are axiomatic theories. In such theories formulas are certain **strings** (that is, finite sequences) of symbols. We require the following properties of formulas.

(I) The notion of *formula* must be effective. That is, there must be an effective procedure for deciding, for an arbitrary string of symbols, whether it is a formula.

(II) The notion of *axiom* must be effective. That is, there must be an effective procedure for deciding, for an arbitrary formula, whether it is an axiom.

(III) The notion of *inference* must be effective. That is, there must be an effective procedure for deciding, for an arbitrary finite sequence of formulas, whether each member of the sequence may be inferred from one or more of those preceding it by a rule of inference.

In such a formal axiomatic theory the notion of *proof* is effective; that is, there is an effective procedure for deciding, for an arbitrary finite sequence of formulas, whether it is a proof. The existence of such an effective procedure does not entail a method for discovering proofs. It merely enables one to decide whether a purported proof is, in fact, a proof.

We do not require the notion of *theorem* to be effective. If there can be found for a theory an effective procedure for deciding, for an arbitrary formula, whether it is a theorem, the theory loses its appeal to mathematicians. For the implication of the notion of theorem being effective is that one can devise a set of preassigned instructions for a machine such that it could check formulas of the theory to determine whether they are theorems. Mathematical logicians have shown that for many interesting axiomatic theories the notion of theorem is not effective. It follows that human inventiveness and ingenuity is necessary in mathematics.

A problem which must be faced in presenting a formal axiomatic theory is how to specify the system of logic to be used. One obvious way is to give the rules of inference. In all interesting systems the set of rules is infinite, and there arises the problem of how to specify the set in such a way that one can determine whether a particular rule is in the set. The solution we shall employ calls for specifying a finite set of rules of inference and adding logical axioms to those of the axiomatic theory for the purpose of generating theorems which express further logical principles. That is, the solution calls for the fusion of an axiomatized system of logic with an axiomatic theory to produce a formal axiomatic theory. Of the systems of logic which might be used in this connection, we shall choose the predicate calculus of first order. Our justification for this choice is that it formalizes most of the logical principles accepted by most mathematicians and that it supplies all the logic necessary for many mathematical theories. In the next two sections we describe an axiomatization.

3.6. The Statement Calculus as a Formal Axiomatic Theory

In view of the role of the statement calculus in a theory of inference (Section 2.4), the goal of an axiomatization is a formal axiomatic theory in which the theorems are precisely the tautologies. This was first achieved by Frege, in 1879. Since then, many formulations have appeared. That which we shall present is due to Whitehead and Russell (*Principia Mathematica*) as modified by P. Bernays. The primitive symbols (or, formal symbols) are:

$$\sim \quad \vee \quad (\quad)$$
$$\mathfrak{A} \quad \mathfrak{B} \quad \mathfrak{C} \quad \mathfrak{A}_1 \quad \mathfrak{B}_1 \quad \mathfrak{C}_1 \quad \cdots$$

The symbols in the second row are called **statement letters.** The three dots, which are not symbols, indicate that the list continues without end. We define formula as follows:

(I) Each statement letter alone is a formula.

(II) If A and B are formulas, then $(A) \vee (B)$ is a formula.

(III) If A is a formula, then $\sim(A)$ is a formula.

(IV) Only strings of formal symbols are formulas. A string of formal symbols is a formula only if its being so follows from (I)–(III).

It can be proved that the notion of formula is effective. The intended interpretation of the statement letters is that they stand for prime statements of some theory. The intended interpretation of a formula is that it stands for some statement. We shall use capital English letters to stand for arbitrary formulas (the convention which was used in the definition of formula). Further conventions include those described earlier regarding the omission of parentheses. Also, we introduce the following abbreviations for certain formulas:

$$A \rightarrow B \text{ for } \sim A \vee B,$$
$$A \wedge B \text{ for } \sim(\sim A \vee \sim B),$$
$$A \leftrightarrow B \text{ for } (A \rightarrow B) \wedge (B \rightarrow A).$$

The axioms for the theory are the following formulas:

(PC1) $\sim(A \vee A) \vee A,$

(PC2) $\sim A \vee (A \vee B),$

(PC3) $\sim(A \vee B) \vee (B \vee A),$

(PC4) $\sim(\sim A \vee B) \vee (\sim(C \vee A) \vee (C \vee B)),$

or, in abbreviated notation,

(PC1) $A \vee A \rightarrow A,$

(PC2) $A \rightarrow (A \vee B),$

(PC3) $A \vee B \rightarrow B \vee A,$

(PC4) $(A \rightarrow B) \rightarrow (C \vee A \rightarrow C \vee B).$

Writing the axioms in terms of arbitrary formulas means that each includes infinitely many axioms, one for each choice of the formulas occurring in the axiom. [This agreement is signaled by referring to each of (PC1)–(PC4) as an **axiom schema.**] For example, by virtue of (PC2), each of

$$\alpha \vee \beta \rightarrow (\alpha \vee \beta) \vee (\alpha_1 \vee \beta_1),$$
$$\alpha \vee \beta \rightarrow (\alpha \vee \beta) \vee (\alpha \vee \beta),$$
$$\sim\alpha \rightarrow \sim\alpha \vee \sim\alpha,$$

is an axiom. Even though there are infinitely many axioms, the notion of axiom is effective, since each axiom must have one of four forms.

The only rule of inference is modus ponens (see the fifth of Examples B, Section 2.4): A and $A \rightarrow B$ have B as an immediate consequence.

The exact form which the definition of deducibility (Section 3.1) takes for the statement calculus is this: A formula B is **deducible** from (assumption) formulas $A_1, A_2, \cdots, A_m$, symbolized by

$$A_1, A_2, \cdots, A_m \vdash B,$$

iff there exists a finite sequence $B_1, B_2, \cdots, B_t$ of formulas such that B_t is B, and for each B_i,

    (i) B_i is an assumption formula, or

    (ii) B_i is an axiom, or

    (iii) B_i is an immediate consequence of two earlier B's.

A sequence such as $B_1, B_2, \cdots, B_t$ is a **demonstration** of $A_1, A_2, \cdots, A_m \vdash B$.

A deduction of a formula B from no assumptions is a proof of B, and B is a theorem. We recall that we have agreed to symbolize this by

$$\vdash B.$$

An illustration of a proof is given next. It is a proof of the formula $\alpha \vee \sim\alpha$. It follows that $\vdash \alpha \vee \sim\alpha$.

(1) $\alpha \vee \alpha \rightarrow \alpha$	Axiom schema (PC1)
(2) $(\alpha \vee \alpha \rightarrow \alpha) \rightarrow$ $(\sim\alpha \vee (\alpha \vee \alpha) \rightarrow \sim\alpha \vee \alpha)$	Axiom schema (PC4)
(3) $\sim\alpha \vee (\alpha \vee \alpha) \rightarrow \sim\alpha \vee \alpha$	1,2 modus ponens
(4) $(\alpha \rightarrow \alpha \vee \alpha) \rightarrow (\alpha \rightarrow \alpha)$	1,2 modus ponens [same as (3)]
(5) $\alpha \rightarrow \alpha \vee \alpha$	Axiom schema (PC2)
(6) $\alpha \rightarrow \alpha$	4,5 modus ponens
(7) $\sim\alpha \vee \alpha$	4,5 modus ponens [same as (6)]

(8) $\sim\!\alpha \vee \alpha \rightarrow \alpha \vee \sim\!\alpha$ Axiom schema (PC3)

(9) $\alpha \vee \sim\!\alpha$ 7,8 modus ponens

When a proof is given an analysis is usually given in parallel, as above. This is not required, however, because there is an effective procedure for supplying an analysis.

We observe that we can just as easily prove $\vdash \mathfrak{B} \vee \sim\!\mathfrak{B}$ or $\vdash (\mathfrak{C} \wedge \alpha) \vee \sim(\mathfrak{C} \wedge \alpha)$ by repeating the above sequence of formulas with $\mathfrak{B}$ or $\mathfrak{C} \wedge \alpha$ in place of α. Indeed, if we repeat the sequence of formulas with any formula A in place of α, we obtain a proof of $A \vee \sim\!A$. The correct names for this last result and its derivation are **theorem schema** and **proof schema**. The point is that A is not a formula of the system, but that it denotes a formula, and what we have suggested as a proof is a recipe for constructing a proof of $A \vee \sim\!A$, where A denotes some fixed but arbitrary formula. Theorem schema, like axiom schema, have the merit that a theorem results when for each letter which appears in it one chooses one and the same formula.

That the proof of such an uncomplicated theorem as $A \vee \sim\!A$ is so long may cause alarm. In general, the development of any axiomatic theory is tedious at the outset, since there is little with which to work. In the theory at hand we are further hampered by having just one rule of inference. In a systematic development the first step is the derivation of further rules of inference which assert the existence of proofs under various conditions. We forego such a development and direct our attention to showing that our formal theory fulfills its intended role.

We shall show first that the concept of deducibility can be reduced to that of provability in a manner parallel to the reduction of the concept of valid consequence to that of validity (Section 2.4). The following theorem, proved by J. Herbrand, in 1930, is the key to the reduction.

THEOREM 3.1 (The Deduction Theorem). If $A_1, A_2, \cdots, A_m \vdash B$, then $A_1, A_2, \cdots, A_{m-1} \vdash A_m \rightarrow B$ and, more generally, $\vdash A_1 \rightarrow (A_2 \rightarrow (\cdots(A_m \rightarrow B)\cdots))$.

The proof of the first implication, which we omit, is by induction on the length of the demonstration which accompanies the assumption that B is deducible from $A_1, A_2, \cdots, A_m$. Repeated application of this result yields the remaining one. The converse of this is the next theorem.

THEOREM 3.2. If $\vdash A_1 \to (A_2 \to (\cdots (A_m \to B) \cdots))$, then $A_1, A_2, \cdots, A_m \vdash B$.

Proof. Assume that $A_1 \to (A_2 \to (\cdots (A_m \to B) \cdots))$ is a theorem and that $C_1, C_2, \cdots, C_t$ is a proof of it. Then the following sequence is a demonstration of $A_1, A_2, \cdots, A_m \vdash B$ (for $m = 3$).

$$
\begin{array}{ll}
(1) & C_1 \\
\cdot & \cdot \\
\cdot & \cdot \\
\cdot & \cdot \\
(t-1) & C_{t-1} \\
(t) & A_1 \to (A_2 \to (A_3 \to B)) \\
(t+1) & A_1 \\
(t+2) & A_2 \to (A_3 \to B) \\
(t+3) & A_2 \\
(t+4) & A_3 \to B \\
(t+5) & A_3 \\
(t+6) & B
\end{array}
$$

These two theorems accomplish the reduction of the notion of deducibility to that of provability. A comparison of the two theorems with the Corollary to Theorem 2.6 shows the parallel between this result and the reduction of the notion of valid consequence to the notion of validity. It follows that if we can show that a formula A is a theorem iff it is a tautology, we will have demonstrated the equivalence of the informal and the formal statement calculus, both by themselves and when applied under a set of assumption formulas. We do this in the next two theorems. First, it may be noted that in the present circumstances we understand a tautology to be a formula such that for every assignment of truth values to its constituent statement letters, it is assigned truth value T in accordance with the truth tables for $\sim$ and $\vee$.

THEOREM 3.3 (The Completeness Theorem). If A is a tautology, then A is provable; that is, if $\vDash A$, then $\vdash A$.

The proof, though elementary, is long; therefore, it will not be given. In contrast, the converse is established easily, as we show next.

THEOREM 3.4.   If A is provable, then A is a tautology; that is, if $\vdash A$, then $\vDash A$.

Proof.   We observe first that each instance of an axiom schema is a tautology; that is, the theorem is true for the axioms. Further, by Theorem 2.3, if $\vDash A$ and $\vDash A \to B$, then $\vDash B$. Since every theorem is either an axiom or comes from the axioms by one or more uses of modus ponens, every theorem is a tautology.

That is, the notions of validity and provability for the statement calculus are co-extensive. This result was proved first in 1921 by the American logician, Emil Post. Since validity can be effectively decided for an arbitrary formula, the notion of theorem in the statement calculus is effective.

We conclude this section with an example of imbedding a system of logic in an axiomatic theory, an idea which was proposed at the end of the preceding section. Namely, we consider the imbedding of the statement calculus in an axiomatic theory. This may be accomplished by:

(i) including among the formation rules for formulas of the theory the following:

If A and B are formulas, then so is $(A) \vee (B)$.
If A is a formula, then so is $\sim(A)$.

(ii) adding to the axioms of the theory the four axiom schemes we have chosen for the statement calculus (where "formula" is now taken in the extended sense of "formula of the theory"),

(iii) adding modus ponens to the rules of inference.

Formulas of the theory may then be regarded as formulas of a statement calculus in which the role of the statement letters is played by those formulas which are not of the form $(A) \vee (B)$ or $\sim(A)$ (that is, formulas which cannot be decomposed into further formulas using $\vee$ and $\sim$ in the way shown).

As a result of the imbedding, every tautology will be a theorem of the theory. More important, the statement calculus is available as a theory of inference. For example, a proof of a formula B may be made by establishing A and $\sim B \to \sim A$ as theorems. Indeed, tautology 2 of Theorem 2.4 implies that A, $\sim B \to \sim A \vdash B$. As another illustration we recall that in the second of Examples B, Section 2.5, the tautology $(\sim B \to C \wedge \sim C) \to B$ was used to justify a proof by contradiction. It may be used for the same purpose in the present circumstances. That is, a proof of B may be made by establishing that $\sim B \vdash C$ and $\vdash \sim C$. Then $\sim B \vdash C \wedge \sim C$, or $\vdash \sim B \to (C \wedge \sim C)$. But from the tautology mentioned, $\sim B \to (C \wedge \sim C) \vdash B$, and, hence, $\vdash B$.

3.7. The Predicate Calculus as a Formal Axiomatic Theory

The axiomatization of the first-order predicate calculus which we present is essentially that devised by Hilbert and Ackermann. It first appeared in their book, *Grundzüge der Theoretichen Logik* (1928); the second edition has been translated into English under the title *Principles of Mathematical Logic*. The primitive symbols are:

$$\sim \quad \vee \quad (\ ) \quad ,$$

an infinite list of (individual) variables:

$$a \quad b \quad c \quad a_1 \quad b_1 \quad c_1 \quad \cdots$$

an infinite list of 1-place predicate letters:

$$\mathcal{A}^1 \quad \mathcal{B}^1 \quad \mathcal{C}^1 \quad \mathcal{A}_1^1 \quad \mathcal{B}_1^1 \quad \mathcal{C}_1^1 \quad \cdots$$

an infinite list of k-place predicate letters, for each positive integer k:

$$\mathcal{A}^k \quad \mathcal{B}^k \quad \mathcal{C}^k \quad \mathcal{A}_1^k \quad \mathcal{B}_1^k \quad \mathcal{C}_1^k \quad \cdots$$

Formula is defined as follows.

(I) If P is an n-place predicate letter and $x_1, x_2, \cdots, x_n$ are variables (not necessarily distinct), then $P(x_1, x_2, \cdots, x_n)$ is a formula.

(II) If A and B are formulas, then so is $(A) \vee (B)$.

(III) If A is a formula, then so is $\sim(A)$.

(IV) If A is a formula and x is a variable, then $(x)A$ is a formula.

(V) Only strings of formal symbols are formulas, and such a string is a formula only if its being so follows from (I)–(IV).

It can be proved that the notion of formula is effective. We make the same definitions and conventions as for the statement calculus. In particular, capital English letters will stand for arbitrary formulas. Further, we introduce

$(\exists x)A$ (as an abbreviation) for $\sim(x) \sim A$.

Also, the notions of a bound occurrence and of a free occurrence of a variable in a formula, and of a variable being bound in a formula and of a variable being free in a formula, are defined as in Section 2.7. The notion of substitution of one variable for another is also carried over. Further, the valuation procedure described in Section 2.8 is applicable and leads to the notion of a valid formula.

The axioms for the theory are the axiom schemata (PC1)–(PC4) of the statement calculus plus the following two schemata.

(PC5) $(x)A(x) \rightarrow A(y)$, where $A(x)$ is any formula such that when the variable y is substituted for x in $A(x)$, none of the resulting occurrences of y is bound, that is, $A(x)$ is free for y.

(PC6) $A(y) \rightarrow (\exists x)A(x)$ with the same restrictions as in (PC5).

As the rules of inference we take modus ponens plus the following two (see Theorem 2.11).

The **rule of generalization.** The formula $B \rightarrow A(x)$ has $B \rightarrow (x)A(x)$ as an immediate consequence, provided that B contains no free occurrences of x.

The **rule of specification.** The formula $A(x) \rightarrow B$ has $(\exists x)A(x) \rightarrow B$ as an immediate consequence, provided that B contains no free occurrence of x.

The definition of deducibility is an extension of that for the statement calculus given in the preceding section. A formula B is **deducible** from (assumption) formulas $A_1, A_2, \cdots, A_m$, symbolized $A_1, A_2, \cdots, A_m \vdash B$, iff there exists a finite sequence $B_1, B_2, \cdots, B_t$ of formulas such that B_t is B and, for each B_i,

(i) B_i is an assumption formula, or

(ii) B_i is an axiom, or

(iii) there exist j and k, with $j < i$ and $k < i$, such that B_k is $B_j \rightarrow B_i$, or

(iv) B_i is $B \rightarrow (x)A(x)$, where there exists a $j < i$ such that B_j is $B \rightarrow A(x)$, and B contains no free occurrences of x, and x is a variable which does not occur free in any assumption formula.

(v) B_i is $(\exists x)A(x) \rightarrow B$, where there exists a $j < i$ such that B_j is $A(x) \rightarrow B$, and the same restrictions on B and x as in (iv) are observed.

The restriction on x in (iv) and (v) may be ignored if B_i precedes all occurrences of $A_1, A_2, \cdots, A_m$ in the deduction. A deduction of a formula B from no assumptions is a proof of B, and B is a theorem. Since modus ponens is among the rules of inference, the theorems of the predicate calculus include those of the statement calculus. That is, every tautology is a theorem, where tautology is to be taken in the sense explained in Section 2.8.

The notion of deducibility can be reduced to that of provability in a manner parallel to that in which the corresponding reduction is made in the statement calculus. Indeed, the deduction theorem, in the form stated as Theorem 3.1, can be extended to the predicate calculus, and the same is true of Theorem 3.2. Taken together, these two extensions settle the matter. It follows that if we can show that $\vDash A$ iff $\vdash A$, we will have demonstrated the equivalence of the informal and the formal predicate calculus, both by themselves and when applied under a set of assumption formulas. As in the statement calculus, the proof is easy in one direction.

THEOREM 3.5. If $\vdash A$ in the predicate calculus, then $\vDash A$.

Proof. As in the proof of the corresponding assertion for the statement calculus (Theorem 3.4), we observe first that the assertion is true for each instance of each axiom schema. In this connection Theorem 2.10 is pertinent. Further, by virtue of Theorem 2.3 (extended to the predicate calculus) and Theorem 2.11, if C is any theorem which has been obtained from a theorem B by application of a rule of inference, and $\vDash B$, then C is valid. Hence, if any formula A is a theorem, then A is valid.

The converse of this result is a consequence of a theorem first proved by K. Gödel, in 1930. Although it is not his most celebrated theorem, is is a remarkable result. We state it without proof as the next theorem.

THEOREM 3.6 (Gödel's completeness theorem for the predicate calculus). For each formula A in the predicate calculus, if $\vDash A$, then $\vdash A$.

3.8. First-order Axiomatic Theories

A **first-order theory** (or, a **theory with standard formalization**) is a formal theory for which the predicate calculus of first order suffices as the logical basis. Those with which we shall be concerned are also axiomatic theories.

An intuitive understanding of the essence of such theories is desirable before technical details are discussed. We take as a starting point for this the description in Section 3.3 of the primitive terms of an informal theory, namely, a set X and certain constants associated with X. We assume that each constant is either an element of X (that is, an individual constant) or a subset of X^n (that is, a relation or an operation in X). Now with an operation in X as well as with a relation in X there can be associated a predicate. For example, with an n-ary relation ρ we associate the predicate letter $P(x_1, x_2, \cdots, x_n)$ such that a prime formula $P(y_1, y_2, \cdots, y_n)$ is assigned the value T for an assignment of u_i to y_i, $i = 1, 2, \cdots, n$, iff $\langle u_1, u_2, \cdots, u_n \rangle \in \rho$. Here, however, we prefer the denotation **predicate symbol** instead of predicate letter, to indicate a predicate letter which is intended to stand for a *fixed* predicate. Henceforth we shall regard the primitive terms of the theory as a set X, a (possibly empty) set of individual constants (members of X), and a set of predicate symbols. Now consider the formal theory whose formal symbols are those individual constants present in the informal theory, an infinite list of individual variables, the predicate symbols defined by the informal theory in the manner suggested above, and the logical symbols of the predicate calculus. As the axioms of the theory we take those of the informal theory together with those of the predicate calculus. As the rules of inference we take those of the predicate calculus. The result is a first-order axiomatic theory! When the predicate calculus is imbedded in a theory as just described, the resulting theory is often called an **applied predicate calculus,** and the untainted version of Section 3.7 is called the **pure predicate calculus.**

Before "firming up" the notion of a first-order theory in the style to which we are trying to accustom the reader, we discuss one preliminary. In most theories which can be axiomatized as first-order theories, there is present the notion of equality. It is efficient to incorporate this at the outset of the pure predicate calculus, and we shall do this now. As it is intuitively understood, "$x = y$" means that x and y are the same object or that "x" and "y" are names of the same object. For mathematical purposes, all that is required of equality is that (i) it be an equivalence relation, and (ii) it have the following substitution property: If $x = y$ and Q is the result of replacing one or more occurrences of "x" in the statement P by occurrences of "y," then Q has the same meaning as P. Now the properties of symmetry and transitivity can be derived from those of reflexivity and substitution. We take this into account in defining the **first-order predicate calculus with equality** as an axiomatic theory. It is the predicate calculus of Section 3.7 with the addition of (i) the predicate symbol $=$ to the formal symbols, (ii) the clause "if x and y are variables, then $(x = y)$ is a formula" to the definition of formula, and (iii) the axiom

(PC7) $(a)(a = a)$

and the axiom schema:

(PC8) If x, y, and z are distinct variables and $A(z)$ is free for x and for y, then $(x)(y)(x = y \rightarrow (A(x) \rightarrow A(y))$.

We can now give a precise description of a first-order theory $\mathfrak{T}$. The formal symbols are the following.

(I_s) A (possibly empty) set of individual constants.

(II_s) An infinite sequence of individual variables, $a_0, a_1, \cdots, a_n \cdots$.

(III_s) A set of predicate symbols, In this set appears $=$.

(IV_s) The logical symbols of the predicate calculus and parentheses.

Each predicate symbol is designated as a **relation symbol** or as an **operation symbol**. An n-place predicate symbol will be called an n-ary relation symbol or an n-ary operation symbol, depending on its designation. In particular, $=$ is classified as a binary relation symbol. The relation symbols together with the operation symbols and the individual constants make up the **nonlogical constants** of $\mathfrak{T}$. The equality symbol together with the logical symbols make up the **logical constants** of $\mathfrak{T}$. The equality symbol, although regarded as a logical constant, is included in the set of relation symbols.

The description of $\mathfrak{T}$ further includes the definition of a **term**. This is given inductively.

(I_t) An individual variable and an individual constant are each terms.

(II_t) If $r_1, r_2, \cdots, r_n$ are terms and A is an n-place operation symbol, then $A(r_1, r_2, \cdots, r_n)$ is a term.

(III_t) The only terms are those given by (I_t) and (II_t).

The definition of **formula** is also given inductively.

(I_f) If A is an n-ary relation symbol and $r_1, r_2, \cdots, r_n$ are terms, then $A(r_1, r_2, \cdots, r_n)$ is a formula. In particular, if r and s are terms, then $(r = s)$ is a formula.

(II$_f$) If A and B are formulas, then so are $\sim(A)$ and $(A) \vee (B)$.

(III$_f$) If A is a formula and x is a variable, then $(x)A$ is a formula.

(IV$_f$) Only strings of symbols and terms are formulas, and such a string is a formula only if its being so follows from (I$_f$)–(III$_f$).

We carry over to $\mathfrak{T}$ all of the abbreviations, conventions, and definitions employed in the predicate calculus. Further, $(r = s)$ will be abbreviated to $r = s$ and $\sim(r = s)$ to $r \neq s$. The only part of the foregoing for which we did not prepare the reader is the notion of a term. Under the intended interpretation, a term is the name of an object. In addition to variables and individual constants being terms, strings composed from variables and individual constants using operation symbols should be terms, since in the intended interpretation they are function values.

For first-order theories it is assumed that the nonlogical constants have an interpretation in some nonempty domain D. Roughly, this means that each individual constant is interpreted as a fixed member of D, that each individual variable has D as its range, that relation symbols have interpretations as subsets of D^n for some n, and that operation symbols have interpretations as functions on D^n (for some n) into D. This will be described in detail along with a valuation procedure (which extends that given in Section 2.8 for the predicate calculus) for a first-order theory.

As the starting point for the valuation procedure for a first-order theory $\mathfrak{T}$ we assume that all nonlogical constants of $\mathfrak{T}$ can be arranged in a (finite or infinite) sequence $\langle C_0, C_1, \cdots, C_n, \cdots \rangle$ without repetitions. Let D be a nonempty set and $\langle \mathcal{C}_0, \mathcal{C}_1, \cdots, \mathcal{C}_n, \cdots \rangle$ be a sequence of objects in one-to-one correspondence with the foregoing sequence and defined in the following way. If C_n is an m-ary relation symbol, then $\mathcal{C}_n$ is a subset of D^m. If C_n is an m-ary operation symbol, then $\mathcal{C}_n$ is a function of D^m into D. If, finally, C_n is an individual constant, then $\mathcal{C}_n$ is simply an element of D. The sequence $\mathfrak{D} = \langle D, \mathcal{C}_0, \mathcal{C}_1, \cdots, \mathcal{C}_n, \cdots \rangle$ is called an **interpretation** of $\mathfrak{T}$; this is simply a refinement of the definition of the same notion given in Section 3.2. Assume now that $\mathfrak{D}$ is an interpretation of $\mathfrak{T}$ and that A is a formula of $\mathfrak{T}$. A sequence $\langle d_0, d_1, \cdots, d_n, \cdots \rangle$ with $d_i \in D$ is said to **satisfy** A in $\mathfrak{D}$ iff one of the following conditions holds.

(I_s) A is of the form $a_i = a_j$, and "d_i" and "d_j" denote the same element of D.

(II_s) A is of the form $B(a_{i_1}, a_{i_2}, \cdots, a_{i_n})$, where B is an n-ary relation symbol and $\langle d_{i_1}, d_{i_2}, \cdots, d_{i_n} \rangle$ is a member of the relation associated with this symbol.

(III_s) A is of the form $B(a_{i_1}, a_{i_2}, \cdots, a_{i_n}) = a_j$, where B is an n-ary operation symbol having the function $f: D^n \to D$ associated with it and $f(d_{i_1}, d_{i_2}, \cdots, d_{i_n}) = d_j$,

(IV_s) A is of the form $\sim B$, where B is a formula which is not satisfied by $\langle d_0, d_1, \cdots, d_n, \cdots \rangle$.

(V_s) A is of the form $B \lor C$, where B and C are formulas of which at least one is satisfied.

(VI_s) A is of the form $(a_k)B$, where B is a formula, and for all d in D, $\langle d_0, \cdots, d_{k-1}, d, d_{k+1}, \cdots \rangle$ satisfies B.

Further, a statement S of $\mathfrak{T}$ is said to be **true** in $\mathfrak{D}$ if every sequence $\langle d_0, d_1, \cdots, d_n, \cdots \rangle$ with d_i in D satisfies S in $\mathfrak{D}$. Under the same conditions we shall say that $\mathfrak{D}$ is a **model** of S, thereby sharpening our earlier definition of this notion.

The foregoing is an extension of the earlier valuation procedure for the predicate calculus. Agreement with this will come as soon as it is recognized that an interpretation $\mathfrak{D}$ of a theory $\mathfrak{T}$ includes the equivalent of an assignment of logical functions (relative to some domain) to the predicate symbols of $\mathfrak{T}$. The circumstances under which a formula S of $\mathfrak{T}$ is classified as true in $\mathfrak{D}$ is an extension of those under which a formula receives truth value $\top$ relative to some assignment of logical functions. Having made contact with the earlier valuation procedure, we shall take over some of the terminology introduced in Sections 2.8 and 2.9. A formula S of $\mathfrak{T}$ is called **valid** if it is true in every interpretation of $\mathfrak{T}$. Also, S is a **valid consequence** of a set Γ of formulas if it is true in every interpretation in which all formulas of Γ are true.

A theory $\mathfrak{T}$ with standard formalization becomes an axiomatic theory when the axioms are given and provability is defined. As axioms for $\mathfrak{T}$ we take all instances of the axiom schemata for the predicate calculus with equality, (PC1)–(PC6) and (PC8) and the axiom (PC7), with the following modifications: We now permit as the "y" of (PC5) and (PC6) in Section 3.7 not merely a variable as described there, but, more generally, any term r such that when it is substituted for (the free occurrences of) x in $A(x)$ with result $A(r)$ no free occurrence of a variable in r becomes a bound occurrence. Further, we introduce a set of **nonlogical axioms,** which provide the mathematical content of the theory. As rules of inference we take those for the predicate calculus. The definitions of provability and deducibility remain unchanged, but these notions are strengthened by the added nonlogical axioms. As in the case of the pure predicate calculus, deducibility has a characterization in terms of provability: If Γ is a set of formulas of $\mathfrak{T}$ and B is a formula of $\mathfrak{T}$, then for B to be deducible from Γ it is necessary and sufficient that Γ be empty and B be a theorem, or else that Γ contain formulas $A_1, A_2, \cdots, A_m$ such that $\vdash A_1 \wedge A_2 \wedge \cdots \wedge A_m \rightarrow B$.

A further significant feature of a first-order axiomatic theory is that *every valid formula is a theorem*. This is the content of Gödel's completeness theorem, which we stated as Theorem 3.6 for the pure predicate calculus.

EXAMPLES

1. Starting with the formulation of group theory given in Exercise 15 of Section 3.4 leads to the following description as a first-order axiomatic theory. To the logical constants (including the equality symbol) we adjoin one individual constant e and one 2-place operation symbol $\cdot$. The terms of the theory are defined as follows. Each variable and each constant is a term, and if r and s are terms, then $r \cdot s$ is a term. The formulas of the theory are those as defined in a predicate calculus plus $(r = s)$, where r and s are terms. The nonlogical axioms are

$$(x)(y)(z)(x \cdot (y \cdot z) = (x \cdot y) \cdot z),$$
$$(x)(e \cdot x = x),$$
$$(x)(\exists y)(y \cdot x = e).$$

Alternatively, if we start with the formulation which is implicit in Exercise 7 of Section 3.2, we are led to the following description. The only nonlogical constant is a binary operation symbol $\cdot$, and the nonlogical axioms are

$$x \cdot (y \cdot z) = (x \cdot y) \cdot z,$$
$$(\exists z)(x = y \cdot z),$$
$$(\exists y)(x = y \cdot z).$$

Here we have followed the standard practice of suppressing those universal quantifiers which are required to reduce each formula to a statement.

Each of the foregoing is a formulation of the **elementary theory of groups.** The word "elementary" signals that the first-order predicate calculus is the system of logic employed. Not all of group theory, as a mathematician knows this discipline, is formalized by the elementary theory of groups. The state of affairs is that in any first-order theory one can quantify only with individual variables, and this is inadequate to formalize certain theorems.

2. Formal number theory formalizes the arithmetic of the non-negative integers. One version (based on Peano's axioms) is the following. The nonlogical constants consist of the individual constant 0, two 2-place operation symbols $+$ and $\cdot$, and the 1-place operation symbol $'$. The nonlogical axioms consist of the following six axioms and one axiom schema.

$$a' = b' \rightarrow a = b,$$
$$a + 0 = a,$$
$$a \cdot 0 = 0,$$
$$a' \neq 0,$$
$$a + b' = (a + b)',$$
$$a \cdot b' = ab + a,$$
$$A(0) \land (x)(A(x) \rightarrow A(x')) \rightarrow A(x),$$

where x is any variable, $A(x)$ is any formula, and $A(0)$, $A(x')$ are the results of substituting $0, x'$ respectively for the free occurrences of x in $A(x)$.

The intended interpretation of the nonlogical constants is the obvious one. It is intended that 0 be the integer zero, that x' be the successor of x (that is, $x + 1$), that $x + y$ be the sum of x and y, and that $x \cdot y$ be their product. The axiom schema is the principle of mathematical induction.

3.9. Metamathematics

The presentation of a formal theory must be given in a language which both writer and reader understand. To point out the obvious, we have chosen the English language for this purpose. The familiar language in which the description of a formal theory is imbedded is called the **metalanguage** (or, **syntax language**); it is used to communicate *about* the theory. The formal symbols of a formal theory constitute the basis for a language which is used to talk *within* the theory; this is called the **object language**. For example, "The elementary theory of groups is an undecidable theory" is a statement about group theory written in the English language, that is, in the metalanguage. In contrast, "$(a)(b)(c)(a \cdot b = a \cdot c \rightarrow b = c)$" is a statement of group theory, that is of the object language. In general terms, the contrast between the metalanguage and the object language of a theory is parallel to the contrast between the English language and the French language for one whose native tongue is English and who has studied French. At the outset, vocabulary, rules of grammar, and so on, are communicated in English (the metalanguage). Later, one begins to write in French, that is, he forms sentences within the object language.

A theorem about a formal theory is called a **metatheorem** and is to be distinguished from the theorems of the theory. It is easy to make this distinction, since a theorem of the theory is written in the symbolism of the theory, whereas a metatheorem is written in English. In the preceding paragraph the statement in English regarding group theory is a metatheorem, and that written in terms of $\cdot$, $=$, and so on, is a theorem of group theory. Since the proof of a metatheorem requires a system of logic, a description of the system of logic should be available for the prospective user of the metatheorem. One possibility is to formalize the metalanguage as we have formalized the predicate calculus. But this entails the use of a metametalanguage, and the beginning of an unending regress is established. The alternative, which was proposed by Hilbert, may be summarized roughly as: In the metalanguage employ an informal system of logic whose principles are universally accepted. The ground rules for such a system of logic can be spelled out quite clearly. First of all, controversial principles, such as proof by contradiction, or Zorn's lemma (see Section 4.5), must not be used. Also, the proof of an existence theorem must be constructive; that is, it must provide an effective procedure for constructing the object which is asserted to exist. More generally, only "finitary" methods of proof may be used; that is, in proofs there should be no reference either to an infinite number of structural properties of formulas or to an infinite number of manipulations with formulas. Further, it is assumed that if, for example, the English language is taken as the metalanguage, then only a minimal fragment will be used. (The danger in permitting all of the English language to be used is that one can derive within it the classical paradoxes, for example, Russell's paradox). **Metamathematics** is the study of formal theories using the kind of logic which fits within such a framework. In brief, metamathematics is the study of formal theories by methods which should be convincing to everyone qualified to engage in such activities.

An example of a metamathematical notion is *consistency*, as defined in Section 3.4. The definition there is applicable to any formal theory which includes the statement calculus. A metatheorem concerning such theories is proved next.

THEOREM 3.7 Let $\mathfrak{T}$ be a formal theory which includes the statement calculus. Then $\mathfrak{T}$ is consistent iff not every formula of $\mathfrak{T}$ is a theorem.

Proof. Suppose that $\mathfrak{T}$ is inconsistent and that A is a formula such that both $\vdash A$ and $\vdash \sim A$. Now $A \rightarrow (\sim A \rightarrow B)$ is a theorem for any B, since it is a tautology. Hence, B, that is, any formula, is a theorem by two applications of modus ponens. For the converse assume that every formula of $\mathfrak{T}$ is a theorem. Then, if A is any formula, both A and $\sim A$ are theorems. Thus, $\mathfrak{T}$ is inconsistent.

Henceforth it will be assumed that all formal theories include the statement calculus, so that Theorem 3.7 will always hold. Our next result is a metatheorem about the statement calculus.

THEOREM 3.8. The statement calculus is a consistent theory.

Proof. Let A be a theorem. Then, in turn, A is a tautology, $\sim A$ is not a tautology, and $\sim A$ is not a theorem.

Exactly the same chain of reasoning gives a proof of the consistency of the predicate calculus. However, for the predicate calculus the proof is *not* metamathematical, because the valuation procedure, on which Theorem 3.5 rests, is *not* effective. A metamathematical proof can be given on observing that the valuation procedure for a fixed finite domain *is* effective, since there are only a finite number of possible assignments for the predicate letters and individual variables in such a domain. We omit this proof, but state the result.

THEOREM 3.9. The predicate calculus of first order is a consistent theory.

Another metamathematical notion is that of completeness. We recall that the intended meaning of this notion is a sufficiency of theorems for some purpose. Two important forms which this takes are that of maximal consistency and that of every valid formula being a theorem. The definition in Section 3.4 is one way in which completeness in the first sense can be formulated. We shall call this **negation completeness**; that is, a formal axiomatic theory is negation complete iff for every formula S of the theory, either $\vdash S$ or $\vdash \sim S$. Another version of completeness in the sense of maximal consistency is this: A formal theory is **absolutely consistent** iff the adjunction, as an axiom, of a formula which is not already a theorem renders the system inconsistent. If we make the definition that a formula S of a theory is **decidable** iff exactly one of S and $\sim S$ is a theorem, then each formula of a theory which is both consistent and negation complete is decidable.

The statement calculus is not negation complete, since neither α nor $\sim \alpha$ is a theorem. It is absolutely complete if we permit ourselves to substitute axiom schemata for axioms. We prove this next.

THEOREM 3.10. If A is any formula of the statement calculus, then either it is a theorem or else the addition of A as an axiom schema results in an inconsistent system.

Proof. Let A be a formula which is not a theorem. We will prove that if A is added as an axiom schema, the system is rendered inconsistent. Since A is not a theorem, it is not a tautology. Therefore, it takes the value F for some row of its truth table. Referring to one such row, we choose an instance of A as follows. Substitute $\alpha \vee \sim \alpha$ for the prime formulas of A which are T, and substitute $\alpha \wedge \sim \alpha$ for those prime formulas which are F. The resulting axiom, B, will always take the value F. Then $\sim B$ is a tautology and hence a theorem. Thus, both B and $\sim B$ are theorems.

The statement calculus is complete in the sense that every valid forula is a theorem; this is simply Theorem 3.3, and the proof is meta-mathematical. The same assertion is true for the predicate calculus (this is Gödel's completeness theorem), but the proof is not metamathematical. The predicate calculus is neither negation complete nor absolutely complete. Metamathematical proofs exist for these assertions.

As background for the final metamathematical notion which we shall discuss we recall the notion of *effective procedure*, as described in Section 3.5. In brief, an effective procedure (or, **decision procedure**) is a method which can be described in advance for providing, in a finite number of steps, a "yes" or "no" answer to any one of a class of questions. The problem of discovering a decision procedure for a given class of questions is called the **decision problem** for that class. Although we require of a formal axiomatic theory that there be a decision procedure for the notion of *proof*, we do not require the same for *provability*. In contrast to the question of whether a given sequence of formulas is a proof (which requires merely the examination of a displayed finite object), the question of whether a given formula is a theorem requires looking elsewhere than *within* the given object for an answer. Further, the definition of a proof sets no bounds on the length of a proof, and to examine all possible proofs without bound on their length is not a procedure which yields an answer to the question in a finite number of steps in the event the formula is not a theorem. This being the state of affairs, the decision problem for provability has special significance for formal theories. Accordingly, it is often called *the* decision problem for a theory. A theory for which the decision problem can be answered in the affirmative is said to be **decidable;** otherwise, it is **undecidable.** An example of a decidable theory is the statement calculus, for since a formula is a theorem iff it is a tautology, the method of truth tables provides an effective procedure. The predicate calculus is an example of an undecidable theory; we shall return to this matter later.

The time has come to fit the role of metamathematics into the scheme of things. We begin by remarking that the discovery that contradictions could be derived within intuitive set theory (that is, that it is an inconsistent theory) came as a shock to many mathematicians. Further, it motivated a few to try to put their houses in order. One such attempt, initiated by E. Zermelo, was to develop set theory as a formal axiomatic theory. Another manifest itself in Russell and Whitehead's *Principia Mathematica*. Zermelo's formal set theory, as modified by succeeding generations, is adequate for developing the set theory which is required for known mathematics and avoids the classical paradoxes to the extent that, as yet, no one has been able to derive them within the theory. However, its consistency has not been demonstrated. The problem of the consistency of such a theory of sets is really the problem of the consistency of classical mathematics, since, as demonstrated (indirectly) in *Principia Mathematica*, classical mathematics can be derived within such a theory of sets. It was Hilbert who distributed on his own shoulders and the shoulders of his co-workers the problem of demonstrating the consistency of classical mathematics. His goal was to formulate classical mathematics as a formal axiomatic theory and then attack the problem of consistency directly. Since a solution in terms of finite models was out of the question, Hilbert proposed as a substitute the use of finitary methods of proof. More precisely, he proposed that consistency be attacked within the confines of metamathematics as described at the beginning of this section. Hilbert's goal, in somewhat more detail, was to create a formal axiomatic theory which is adequate for deriving extant mathematics and is consistent and, finally, is complete in the sense that every formula is theoretically decidable (that is, either it or its negation is a theorem). In Section 3.4 it was pointed out that the consistency of a major part of classical mathematics can be reduced to that of the arithmetic of natural numbers (in brief, **number theory**) as this theory is embodied in the Peano axioms or in a theory of sets sufficiently rich for the derivation of the Peano axioms. After some partial successes at proving the consistency of number theory, hopes for the sought-after result were dashed by a result obtained by Gödel in 1931. This result asserts the impossibility of proving the consistency of a formal theory which includes number theory by constructive methods "formalizable within the theory itself." Regarding such methods, it suffices to say here that as far as is known they incorporate all the principles of logic permissible in metamathematics. Thus, a proof of the consistency of number theory or classical analysis by metamathematics appears to be impossible.

This outstanding result is but a corollary of an even more remarkable theorem proved by Gödel. The major result (Gödel's incompleteness theorem) dealt an even more devastating blow to the entire Hilbert program, for it states, rather loosely, that any consistent formal theory adequate for number theory is incomplete. The principal ingredient of this proof is a statement S of number theory such that neither S nor $\sim S$ is a theorem, thereby proving the theory negation incomplete. Since S and $\sim S$ are statements (and not merely formulas), one is true and the other is false when interpreted as number-theoretic statements. Since neither is provable, there is a true statement of number theory which is not provable. In other words, number theory has an undecidable statement.

One might think that the defect of incompleteness of a theory adequate for number theory could be remedied by adjoining as an axiom either S or $\sim S$, where S is an undecidable statement. But Gödel proved that a theory adequate for number theory must have an undecidable statement. After the adjunction of an undecidable statement as an axiom to such a theory, the resulting theory is still adequate for number theory, and there is still an undecidable statement.

We conclude with an introduction to a second monumental theorem of metamathematics, a theorem proved in 1936 by the American logician, Alonzo Church. This result asserts that there is no effective procedure for deciding, for a formal theory which includes number theory, whether an arbitrary formula is a theorem. It is an "impossibility theorem" similar in nature to the theorem which states that there is no method for trisecting an arbitrary angle with ruler and compass alone. But it differs from the usual impossibility theorem in one fundamental respect: Church's *precise* definition of an effective procedure (a necessary preliminary to his proof) seems to include every computational form which one might attach to this somewhat vague intuitive concept. (Incidentally, the proposition that Church's precise description of an effective procedure is the appropriate one is known as **Church's thesis**).

Gödel's theorem of 1931 follows readily from Church's theorem. Further, Church's theorem can be used to show that the predicate calculus is an undecidable theory. Since 1936, others have proved that a great variety of algebraic theories, including elementary group theory and lattice theory (to mention two theories which we have described) are undecidable.

Chapter 4

Boolean Algebras

THE THEORY OF Boolean algebras has historical as well as present-day practical importance. For the beginner its exposition should prove a serviceable vehicle for assimilating many of the concepts discussed in general terms in Chapter 3. Moreover, it illustrates the important type of axiomatic theory known as an "algebraic theory." The theory of Boolean algebras is, on one hand, relatively simple and, on the other hand, exceedingly rich in structure. Thus, its detailed study serves in some respects as an excellent introduction to techniques which one may employ in the development of a specific axiomatic theory. The only possible shortcoming is that the ease with which it may be put into a relatively completed form is somewhat misleading, insofar as axiomatic theories in general are concerned.

This chapter presents first a natural formulation of the theory. Then a formulation which is commonly regarded as being more elegant is given. This second formulation is used to develop the next topic, the representation theory for Boolean algebras in terms of algebras of sets. Next, the statement calculus is presented as another type of model of the theory and, in conclusion, the notion of a free Boolean algebra is presented.

4.1. A Definition of a Boolean Algebra

By an **algebra of sets** based on U we shall mean a nonempty collection $\mathcal{Q}$ of subsets of the nonempty set U such that if A, $B \in \mathcal{Q}$, then $A \cup B$, $A \cap B \in \mathcal{Q}$, and if $A \in \mathcal{Q}$, then $\overline{A} \in \mathcal{Q}$. For example, the power set of U, $\mathcal{P}(U)$, is an algebra of sets. However, certain proper subsets of $\mathcal{P}(U)$ may be an algebra of sets (see Exercise 6, Section 4.2). If $\mathcal{Q}$ is an algebra of sets based on U, then $U \in \mathcal{Q}$ (since if $A \in \mathcal{Q}$, then $U = A \cup \overline{A} \in \mathcal{Q}$) and $\varnothing \in \mathcal{Q}$ (since if $A \in \mathcal{Q}$, then $\varnothing = A \cap \overline{A} \in \mathcal{Q}$). Further, Theorem 1.1 may be interpreted as a list of properties of an algebra of sets. That this is a fundamental list of properties is suggested by the variety of other properties (for example, those in Theorem 1.2) which may be deduced solely from them. As formulated below, the theory of Boolean algebras may be regarded as the axiomatized version of algebras of sets when viewed as systems having the properties appearing in Theorem 1.1.

We shall say that $\mathfrak{B}$ is a **Boolean algebra** iff $\mathfrak{B}$ is an ordered triple $\langle B, \cup, \cap \rangle$, where B is a set, $\cup$ is a binary operation (called **union** or **join**) in B, $\cap$ is a binary operation (called **intersection** or **meet**) in B, and the following axioms are satisfied. †

(i) Each operation is associative: for all $a, b, c \in B$

$$a \cup (b \cup c) = (a \cup b) \cup c \text{ and } a \cap (b \cap c) = (a \cap b) \cap c.$$

(ii) Each operation is commutative: for all $a, b \in B$

$$a \cup b = b \cup a \text{ and } a \cap b = b \cap a$$

(iii) Each operation distributes over the other: for all $a, b, c \in B$

$$a \cup (b \cap c) = (a \cup b) \cap (a \cup c)$$

and

$$a \cap (b \cup c) = (a \cap b) \cup (a \cap c).$$

(iv) There exist distinct members 0 and 1 of B such that

$$a \cup 0 = a \quad \text{and} \quad a \cap 1 = a, \quad \text{for all } a \in B.$$

† It is intended that (i)–(v) be regarded as ten axioms. To simplify their presentation, they have been grouped into five pairs.

(v) For each element a of B and each pair 0,1 satisfying (iv), there exists an element a' of B such that

$$a \cup a' = 1 \quad \text{and} \quad a \cap a' = 0.$$

A few comments about the axiomatic theory and the formulation set forth are in order. The consistency of the theory can be established by choosing for B the power set of a finite set U having at least one member, taking $\cup$ and $\cap$ as set-union and set-intersection and 0 and 1 as $\varnothing$ and U and, finally, choosing for a' the relative complement of a in U. The uniqueness of the two elements postulated in (iv) is established in Theorem 4.1. These uniquely determined elements are called the **zero element** and **unit element,** respectively, of a Boolean algebra. It was in anticipation of this uniqueness and terminology that the symbols "0" and "1" were used in the axioms. We might have postulated their uniqueness; however, we would then be obligated to prove uniqueness as part of any verification that an alleged Boolean algebra is truly just that. An element a' related to a as specified by axiom (v) is a **complement** of a—that each element has a unique complement is proved below. The set of axioms is not independent since the two associative laws can be derived from the remaining axioms as theorems. A hint as to how this can be done is given in an exercise accompanying the next section. The set of remaining axioms, of which there are really eight displayed as four pairs, is an independent set. This was first established by E.V. Huntington, in 1904, with appropriate examples.

EXERCISE

Accepting for the moment the assertion made in the text that the associative laws (i) in the formulation of the theory of Boolean algebras are redundant, the independence of the remaining set of eight axioms can be demonstrated by a collection of eight systems of the form $\langle B, \cup, \cap \rangle$, the first of which satisfies all of (ii)–(v) except the commutativity of $\cup$, the second of which satisfies all of (ii)–(v) except the commutativity of $\cap$, and so on. For a B having just a few elements, an operation in B may be exhibited by means of a "multiplication table," that is, a square array whose rows and columns are numbered with the elements of B and such that at the intersection of the ath row and the

b^{th} column the composite of a and b appears. For example, the following two tables define two operations in the set $B = \{a,b\}$.

∪	a	b		∩	a	b
a	a	b		a	a	a
b	b	a		b	a	b

Show that $\langle B,\cup,\cap \rangle$, with a as 0 and b as 1, satisfies all of (ii)–(v) except the first half of (iii), thereby demonstrating the independence of this axiom. Again, show that $\langle B,\cup,\cap \rangle$, where $B = \{a,b\}$ and

∪	a	b		∩	a	b
a	a	b		a	b	a
b	b	b		b	a	b

demonstrates the independence of the second half of (iii). Construct six other systems which demonstrate the independence of the other axioms.

4.2. Several Basic Properties of a Boolean Algebra

As a preliminary to a systematic development of theorems for the theory of Boolean algebras, starting with the formulation given, the principle of duality should be pointed out. Defining the **dual** of a statement formulated within the framework of a Boolean algebra as the statement that results on the replacement of ∪ by ∩ and ∩ by ∪, 1 by 0 and 0 by 1 throughout, we observe that each axiom is a dual pair of assumptions. Hence, if T is any theorem for Boolean algebras, then the dual of T is a theorem, the duals of the steps appearing in the proof of T providing a proof of the dual. This **principle of duality** for Boolean algebras yields a free theorem for each theorem which has been proved, unless the theorem happens to be its own dual. As the first theorems for Boolean algebras one may take the assertion of the general commutative law, the general associative law, and the general distributive law, for each operation. These are proved exactly as indicated after Theorem 1.1. Next, the uniqueness of 0 and 1 can be established, and then the assertions appearing in Theorem 1.2 can be proved. This is done below, in part.

THEOREM 4.1.   In each Boolean algebra $\langle B, \cup, \cap \rangle$ the following hold.

   (vi) The elements 0 and 1 are unique.
  (vii) Each element has a unique complement.
 (viii) For each element a, $(a')' = a$.
   (ix) $0' = 1$ and $1' = 0$.
    (x) For each element a, $a \cup a = a$ and $a \cap a = a$.
   (xi) For each element a, $a \cup 1 = 1$ and $a \cap 0 = 0$.
  (xii) For all a and b, $a \cup (a \cap b) = a$ and $a \cap (a \cup b) = a$.
 (xiii) For all a and b, $(a \cup b)' = a' \cap b'$ and $(a \cap b)' = a' \cup b'$.

Proof.   For (vi) assume that 0_1 and 0_2 are elements of B such that $a \cup 0_1 = a$ and $a \cup 0_2 = a$ for all a. Then $0_2 \cup 0_1 = 0_2$ and $0_1 \cup 0_2 = 0_1$. By axiom (ii), $0_2 \cup 0_1 = 0_1 \cup 0_2$, and, hence, $0_2 = 0_1$. Thus there is a single element in B satisfying the first property in (iv). (The uniqueness of 1 follows by the principle of duality.)

For (vii) assume that a_1' and a_2' are both complements of a. Then

$$
\begin{aligned}
a_1' &= a_1' \cup 0, & &\text{by (iv);} \\
     &= a_1' \cup (a \cap a_2'), & &\text{since } a \cap a_2' = 0; \\
     &= (a_1' \cup a) \cap (a_1' \cup a_2'), & &\text{by (iii);} \\
     &= (a \cup a_1') \cap (a_1' \cup a_2'), & &\text{by (ii);} \\
     &= 1 \cap (a_1' \cup a_2'), & &\text{since } a \cup a_1' = 1; \\
     &= (a_1' \cup a_2') \cap 1, & &\text{by (ii);} \\
     &= a_1' \cup a_2', & &\text{by (iv).}
\end{aligned}
$$

By a similar proof we get

$$a_2' = a_2' \cup a_1'.$$

Hence, by (ii), $a_1' = a_2'$.

For (viii), by definition of the complement of a, $a \cup a' = 1$ and $a \cap a' = 0$. Hence, by (ii), $a' \cup a = 1$ and $a' \cap a = 0$. That is, $(a')' = a$, by (vii).

The proof of (ix) is left as an exercise.

The proof of (x) is the following computation.

$$
\begin{aligned}
a \cup a &= (a \cup a) \cap 1, && \text{by (iv);} \\
&= (a \cup a) \cap (a \cup a'), && \text{by (v);} \\
&= a \cup (a \cap a'), && \text{by (iii);} \\
&= a \cup 0, && \text{by (v);} \\
&= a, && \text{by (iv).}
\end{aligned}
$$

The proofs of the remaining parts of the theorem are left as exercises.

The properties of complementation stated in (vii), (viii), and (xiii) can be reformulated in a way that is worthy of note. The fact that each element of a Boolean algebra has a unique complement means that $\{\langle a, a'\rangle | a \in B\}$ is a function on B into B (that is, complementation is a unary operation in B). According to (viii), this function is of period 2 and, consequently, one-to-one and onto. In order to restate (xiii) as we intend, a preliminary remark is necessary. The discussion of the concept of isomorphism in Section 3.3, especially the definition I_2, immediately suggests a definition of the isomorphism of two Boolean algebras. The Boolean algebra $\langle B, \cup, \cap \rangle$ is isomorphic to the Boolean algebra $\langle B^*, \cup^*, \cap^* \rangle$ iff there exists a one-to-one correspondence g between B and B^* such that if $a, b \in B$, then

$$
g(a \cup b) = g(a) \cup^* g(b) \text{ and } g(a \cap b) = g(a) \cap^* g(b)
$$

Clearly, this definition is applicable to the case where the two algebras are one and the same. Now the function defined above resembles an isomorphism of $\langle B, \cup, \cap \rangle$ with itself according to (xiii), except that operations are interchanged in the images of the join and meet. This phenomenon is of sufficient importance as to deserve a name—**anti-isomorphism.** Thus, (xiii) may be summarized by the statement that the mapping $a \rightarrow a'$ is an anti-isomorphism of the algebra with itself.

It is possible to introduce into the set B of an arbitrary Boolean algebra $\langle B, \cup, \cap \rangle$ a partial ordering relation which resembles that of set inclusion. The characterization of inclusion in Theorem 1.3 in terms of set intersection is the origin of the following definition. If $\langle B, \cup, \cap \rangle$ is a Boolean algebra, then for $a, b \in B$

$$
a \leq b \text{ iff } a \cap b = a.
$$

There is no need to give preference to the meet operation, since, just as for the algebra of sets,

$$a \cap b = a \text{ iff } a \cup b = b.$$

The proof of this as well as the proofs of such related facts as

$$a \leq b \text{ iff } a \cap b' = 0 \text{ and } a \leq b \text{ iff } b' \leq a'$$

are left as exercises. Important features of the new relation are stated in the next theorem.

THEOREM 4.2. If $\langle B, \cup, \cap \rangle$ is a Boolean algebra, then $\langle B, \leq \rangle$ is a partially ordered set with greatest element (namely, 1) and least element (namely, 0). Moreover, each pair $\{a,b\}$ of elements has a least upper bound (namely, $a \cup b$) and a greatest lower bound (namely, $a \cap b$).

Proof. The proof is straightforward and is left as an exercise.

EXERCISES

1. Referring to Theorems 1.2 and 4.1, it is obvious that (viii)–(xiii) of Theorem 4.1 are the abstract versions of 8, 8′–13, 13′ of Theorem 1.2. Show that (vi) and (vii) of Theorem 4.1 are the abstractions of 6, 6′ and 7, 7′, respectively, of Theorem 1.2.

2. Supply proofs for parts (ix), (xi), and (xii) of Theorem 4.1.

3. In regard to a proof of the assertion that the associative laws for $\cup$ and $\cap$ can be derived from the remaining axioms for a Boolean algebra, we observe first that the given proofs of (vi)–(viii) and (x) do not employ (i). Further, the proofs called for in the preceding exercise need not use (i). Hence, (ii)–(xii) are available to prove (i). Supply such a proof. Hint: Given a, b, and c, define

$$x = a \cup (b \cup c) \text{ and } y = (a \cup b) \cup c,$$

and then deduce, in turn, that $a \cap x = a \cap y$, $a' \cap x = a' \cap y$, $x = y$.

4. Establish each of the following as a theorem for Boolean algebras.

    (a) $a \leq b$ iff $a \cup b = b$.
    (b) $a \leq b$ iff $a \cap b' = 0$ iff $a' \cup b = 1$.
    (c) $a \leq b$ iff $b' \leq a'$.
    (d) For given x and y, $x = y$ iff $0 = (x \cap y') \cup (y \cap x')$.

5. Prove Theorem 4.2.

6. Let $\mathfrak{A}$ be the collection of all subsets A of $\mathbf{Z}^+$ such that either A or $\overline{A}$

is finite. Show that $\langle \mathcal{C}, \cup, \cap \rangle$, where the operations are the familiar set-theoretical union and intersection, is a Boolean algebra.

Remark. The remaining problems in this section are concerned with a type of generalization of a Boolean algebra called a **lattice**. A lattice is a triple $\langle X, \cup, \cap \rangle$, where X is a nonempty set, $\cup$ and $\cap$ are binary operations in X (read "union" and "intersection," respectively) and the following axioms are satisfied. For all a, b, $c \in X$,

L_1. $a \cup (b \cup c) = (a \cup b) \cup c$;　　L_1'. $a \cap (b \cap c) = (a \cap b) \cap c$;
L_2. $a \cup b = b \cup a$;　　　　　　　　L_2'. $a \cap b = b \cap a$;
L_3. $(a \cup b) \cap a = a$;　　　　　　　L_3'. $(a \cap b) \cup a = a$.

7. State and prove a principle of duality for a lattice.
8. Verify the following properties of a lattice.
   (a) For all a, $a \cup a = a$ and $a \cap a = a$.
   (b) For all a,b, the relations $a \cup b = a$ and $a \cap b = b$ are equivalent.
   (c) For all a,b, the relations $a \cap b = a$ and $a \cup b = b$ are equivalent.

9. Let $\langle X, \leq \rangle$ be a partially ordered set such that each pair of elements has a least upper bound and a greatest lower bound in X. Thus, if we set $a \cup b = \mathrm{lub}\{a,b\}$ and $a \cap b = \mathrm{glb}\{a,b\}$, then $\cup$ and $\cap$ are operations in X. Prove that $\langle X, \cup, \cap \rangle$ is a lattice. Next, prove that, conversely, if in a lattice $\langle X, \cup, \cap \rangle$ we define the relation $\leq$ by $a \leq b$ iff $a \cap b = a$, then $\langle X, \leq \rangle$ is a partially ordered set such that each pair of elements has a least upper bound (namely, $a \cup b$) and a greatest lower bound (namely, $a \cap b$).

Remark. This result gives, in effect, a second formulation of the axiomatic theory called lattice theory. Thus, one may think of a lattice in either way. If the formulation is in terms of $\leq$, then, by $\cup$ and $\cap$, one understands the operations in Exercise 9. If the formulation is in terms of $\cup$ and $\cap$, then, by $\leq$, one understands the ordering relation defined, again, in Exercise 9.

10. Let $\langle X, \cup, \cap \rangle$ and $\langle X', \cup', \cap' \rangle$ be lattices. Show that they are isomorphic iff $\langle X, \leq \rangle$ and $\langle X', \leq' \rangle$ are isomorphic.

11. Show that there are exactly five nonisomorphic lattices of fewer than five elements and that there are exactly five nonisomorphic lattices of five elements. (Hint: For this problem it is more convenient to think of a lattice as a partially ordered set.)

4.3. Another Formulation of the Theory

The formulation which we have given of the theory of Boolean algebras has much to recommend it. The primitive terms are few, and the simplicity and symmetry of the axioms lend aesthetic appeal. Moreover, if the associative laws are omitted, the resulting set is independent. Finally, the formulation clearly reflects the type of system that motivated it. However, it is always a challenge to see if a formulation can be pared down in one or more respects. In the case of Boolean algebras this challenge has been successfully met by a great variety of formulations. We shall describe one that has become quite popular. It achieves for arbitrary Boolean algebras the analogue of the familiar fact for an algebra of sets that either of the operations of union and intersection can be eliminated in terms of the other together with complementation (for example, $A \cup B = (\overline{\overline{A} \cap \overline{B}})$).

If $\langle B, \cup, \cap \rangle$ is a Boolean algebra, then B is a set with at least two distinct members, by (iv). Moreover, the binary operation $\cap$ and the unary operation $'$ have the following properties.

$\cap$ is commutative.

$\cap$ is associative.

For a, b in B, if $a \cap b' = c \cap c'$ for some c in B, then $a \cap b = a$.

For a, b in B, if $a \cap b = a$, then $a \cap b' = c \cap c'$ for all c in B.

The first two properties are axioms, and the last two follow from the facts that for all c in B, $c \cap c' = 0$, and $a \cap b' = 0$ iff $a \cap b = a$. We shall prove next that a triple $\langle B, \cap, ' \rangle$ having the properties mentioned above (a precise description appears in the next theorem) may be taken as a formulation of the theory of Boolean algebras. That is, the primitive terms of the initial formulation of the theory can be defined and the axioms (i)–(v) can be derived as theorems.

THEOREM 4.3. The following is a formulation of the theory of Boolean algebras. The primitive terms are an unspecified set B of at least two elements, a binary operation $\cap$ in B, and a unary operation $'$ in B. The axioms are as follows.

B_1. $\cap$ is a commutative operation.

B_2. $\cap$ is an associative operation.

B_3. For all a, b in B, if $a \cap b' = c \cap c'$ for some c in B, then $a \cap b = a$.

B_4. For all a, b in B, if $a \cap b = a$, then $a \cap b' = c \cap c'$ for all c in B.

Proof. It remains to prove that the primitive terms of the original formulation can be defined and the axioms derived from a triple $\langle B, \cap, ' \rangle$ satisfying B_1–B_4. As the undefined set and the meet operation of the original formulation we take B and $\cap$, respectively. A join operation is defined below. The first ten results below (T1–T10) about $\langle B, \cap, ' \rangle$, together with B_1 and B_2, establish the validity of all axioms of the original formulation except the distributive laws. The remainder of the proof is concerned with them. A telegraphic style of presentation is used for ease in reading.

T1. $a \cap a = a$.
  Pr. $a \cap a' = a \cap a'$. Now apply B_3.

T2. $a \cap a' = b \cap b'$.
  Pr. T1 and B_4.

This result justifies the following definition.

D1. $0 = a \cap a'$ and $1 = 0'$.

T3. $a \cap 0 = 0$.

  Pr. $\begin{aligned} a \cap 0 &= a \cap (a \cap a'), && \text{by } D_1; \\ &= (a \cap a) \cap a', && \text{by } B_2; \\ &= 0, && \text{by T1 and D1.} \end{aligned}$

T_4. $a'' = a$.

  Pr.
  1. $a'' \cap a' = 0$, from D1 and B_1.
  2. $a'' \cap a = a''$, from 1 by B_3.
  3. $a'''' \cap a'' = a''''$, from 2.
  4. $a'''' \cap a = a''''$, from 2 and 3.
  5. $a'''' \cap a' = 0$, from 4, by B_4 and D1.
  6. $a' \cap a''' = a'$, from 5, by B_1 and B_3.
  7. $a''' \cap a' = a'''$, from 2.
  8. $a''' = a'$, from 6 and 7.
  9. $a \cap a''' = 0$, from 8 and D1.
  10. $a \cap a'' = a$, from 9 by B_3.
  11. $a'' = a$, from 2 and 10, by B_1.

T5. $a \cap 1 = a$.

  Pr. $a \cap (a \cap a')'' = 0$, by T4, T1, and D1.

$$a \cap (a \cap a')' = a, \qquad \text{from the above, by } B_3.$$
$$a \cap 1 = a, \qquad \text{by D1.}$$

T6. $\qquad 0 \neq 1.$

Pr. 1. Assume $0 = 1$.

2. $a \cap 0 = a,$ $\qquad$ from 1 and T5.

3. $a \cap 0 = 0,$ $\qquad$ by T3.

4. $a = 0,$ $\qquad$ from 2 and 3.

5. This contradicts the assumption that there exists at least two distinct elements in B.

D2. $\qquad a \cup b = (a' \cap b')'.$

T7. $\qquad (a \cup b)' = a' \cap b'$ and $(a \cap b)' = a' \cup b'.$

Pr. Both follow from D2 and T4.

T8. $\qquad a \cup b = b \cup a$ and $a \cup (b \cup c) = (a \cup b) \cup c.$

Pr. The first follows from B_2, and the second follows from B_3 and T4.

T9. $\qquad a \cup a' = 1.$

Pr. This follows from D2, T4, B_1, and D1.

T10. $\qquad a \cup 0 = a.$

Pr. This follows from D2, D1, and T4.

T11. $\qquad a \cap (a \cup b) = a.$

Pr. 1. $b' \cap (a \cap a') = 0,$ $\qquad$ by T3 and D1.

2. $a \cap (a' \cap b') = 0,$ $\qquad$ from 1, by B_1 and B_2.

3. $a \cap (a' \cap b')'' = 0,$ $\qquad$ from 2, by T4.

4. $a \cap (a' \cap b')' = a,$ $\qquad$ from 3, by B_3.

5. $a \cap (a \cup b) = a,$ $\qquad$ from 4, by D2.

T12. $\qquad a \cap (a \cap b)' = a \cap b'.$

Pr. 1. $a \cap b'' \cap (a \cap b)' = 0,$ $\qquad$ by D1 and T4.

2. $a \cap (a \cap b)' \cap b'' = 0,$ $\qquad$ from 1, by B_1.

3. $a \cap (a \cap b)' \cap b'$
$= a \cap (a \cap b)',$ $\qquad$ from 2, by B_3.

4. $a \cap b' \cap (a \cap b)'$
$= a \cap (a \cap b)',$ $\qquad$ from 3, by B_1.

5. $a \cap b' \cap (a \cap b)'$
$= a \cap b' \cap (b' \cup a'),$ $\qquad$ by T7 and B_1.

6. $a \cap b' \cap (b' \cup a') = a \cap b',$ $\qquad$ by T11.

7. $a \cap (a \cap b)' = a \cap b',$ $\qquad$ from 4, 5, and 6.

T13. $a \cap c = a$, $a \cap c' = 0$ and $a \cup c = c$ are equivalent properties.

Pr.   Left as an exercise.

T14. $a \cap c = a$ and $b \cap c = b$ imply $(a \cup b) \cap c = a \cup b$.

Pr.   Assume that $a \cap c = a$ and $b \cap c = b$. Then $a \cup c = c$ and $b \cup c = c$, by T13. By T11,

$$(a \cup b) \cap [(a \cup b) \cup c] = a \cup b.$$

Two substitutions within the brackets give the desired result.

T15. $a \cap (b \cup c) = (a \cap b) \cup (a \cap c)$ and $a \cup (b \cap c) = (a \cup b) \cap (a \cup c)$.

Pr.   1. $(a \cap b) \cap [a \cap (b \cup c)]$
$= a \cap b \cap (b \cup c) = a \cap b$,   by B_2, T1, and T11.

2. $(a \cap c) \cap [a \cap (b \cup c)] = a \cap c$, similarly.

3. $[(a \cap b) \cup (a \cap c)] \cap [a \cap (b \cup c)]$
$= [(a \cap b) \cup (a \cap c)]$,   from 1, 2, and T14.

4. $[a \cap (b \cup c)] \cap [(a \cap b) \cup (a \cap c)]'$
$= a \cap (b \cup c) \cap (a \cap b)' \cap (a \cap c)'$,
    by T7.
$= a \cap b' \cap c' \cap (b \cup c)$,   by B_1 and T12.
$= a \cap (b \cup c)' \cap (b \cup c)$,
$= 0$.

5. $[a \cap (b \cup c)] \cap [(a \cap b) \cup (a \cap c)]$
$= a \cap (b \cup c)$,   from 4 by T13.

6. $a \cap (b \cup c)$
$= (a \cap b) \cup (a \cap c)$,   from 3 and 5 by B_1.

The proof of the other distributive law is left as an exercise.

The set of axioms in the new formulation of the theory of Boolean algebras is independent. A proof of this requires the determination of a system $\langle B, \cap, ' \rangle_i$, which satisfies all of the axioms except B_i, $i = 1,2,3,4$. Below are defined four systems which demonstrate the independence of the axiom with the corresponding label.

(B₁) $B = \{a,b,c\}$

∩	a	b	c
a	a	a	a
b	a	b	b
c	a	c	c

′	
a	b
b	a
c	a

(B₂) $B = \{a,b,c\}$

∩	a	b	c
a	a	c	b
b	c	b	a
c	b	a	c

′	
a	a
b	c
c	b

(B₃) $B = \{a,b\}$

∩	a	b
a	a	b
b	b	b

′	
a	b
b	b

(B₄) $B = \{A \in \mathcal{P}(\mathbf{Z}^+) \mid \mathbf{Z}^+ - A \text{ is a finite set}\}$

∩ is set intersection

′ is defined as follows. We note that for each A in B there exists a least positive integer a such that $[a]$, the set of all integers $x \geq a$, is included in A. Then A is the disjoint union of $[a]$ and A_0, a subset of $\{1, 2, \cdots, a - 2\}$ (unless $A = \mathbf{Z}^+$, in which case $A = [1]$). Now we define A' to be $A_0' \cup [a + 1]$, where A_0' is the complement of A_0 in $\{1, 2, \cdots, a - 1\}$ (unless $A = \mathbf{Z}^+$, in which case $A' = [2]$).

Some hints for the analysis of this example, which establishes the independence of B₄, appear in an exercise. Possible substitutes for B₄ are described in another exercise.

EXERCISES

1. Prove T13 and the remaining distributive law in the proof of Theorem 4.3.

2. Regarding the system $\langle B, \cap, ' \rangle$, which, it is asserted, establishes the independence of B₄, it is clear that B₁ and B₂ hold. Prove that the system satisfies B₃ but not B₄. Hint: for B₃, show that if $C = C_0 \cup [c]$, then $C \cap C' = [c + 1]$, and, if $A = A_0 \cup [a]$ and $B = B_0 \cup [b]$, then

$$A \cap B' = \begin{cases} (A \cap B_0') \cup [b + 1] & \text{if } a \leq b \\ (A_0 \cap B') \cup [a] & \text{if } a > b \end{cases}$$

3. Show that each of B₅, B₆, $\cdots$, B₁₀ defined below implies B₄ in the presence of B₁, B₂, and B₃. Infer that each of B₅, B₆, $\cdots$, B₉ together

with B_1, B_2, and B_3 yields a formulation of the theory of Boolean algebras.

B_5. For all a and b, $a \cap a' = b \cap b'$.

B_6. For all a, $a'' = a$.

B_7. There exists in B an element m such that whenever $x \cap m = x$, $x = m$.

B_8. There exists an integer $n > 1$ such that for all a, the nth iteration of a under $'$ is equal to a.

B_9. For all a and b, $a \leq b$ implies $b' \leq a'$ (defining $a \leq b$ iff $a \cap b = a$).

B_{10}. B is finite.

4.4. Congruence Relations for a Boolean Algebra

We turn to an examination of an aspect of the two given sets of axioms for a Boolean algebra that has not been touched on. It is sufficient to consider the second set of axioms, since the reader will readily see what alterations are required for our remarks to apply to the first set. When the statements labeled B_1, B_2, B_3, and B_4 were introduced no mention was made of the precise meaning to be assigned the relation symbolized by "$=$"; rather, it was intended that the reader supply his own version of equality. Suppressing any preconceived notions that we might have in this connection, let us determine a set of conditions which are adequate for our purposes. An analysis of the proofs of T1–T15 in the proof of Theorem 4.3 reveals that the following is a sufficient set of conditions.

(E) "$=$" is an equivalence relation.

(S) Let F be an element of the Boolean algebra $\langle B, \cap, ' \rangle$ resulting from elements a, b, $\cdots$ of B using the operations in B, and let $a = a_1$, $b = b_1$, $\cdots$. Then, if F_1 is an element which results from F by the replacement of some or all occurrences of a by a_1, b by b_1, $\cdots$, then $F = F_1$.

Now (S) can be derived from the following two simple instances of this substitution principle.

(C) If $a = b$, then $a \cap c = b \cap c$ for all c.
    If $a = b$, then $a' = b'$.

The proof, which we forego, is by induction on the number of symbols in the element F. Thus (E) and (C) insure (E) and (S), and, hence

(E) together with (C), which are clearly necessary properties of equality, are also sufficient for our purposes. As such, equality is an instance of a congruence relation for a Boolean algebra, a notion which we discuss next.

Before focusing our attentions on congruence relations for Boolean algebras we make several remarks about this concept in a general setting. When one is presented with, or constructs, some specific mathematical system, there is among its ingredients a "natural" congruence relation either explicitly or implicitly defined. This means there is present an equivalence relation which is preserved under the operations at hand in the sense suggested by (C) above. Normally one symbolizes this relation by " $=$," calls it equality, and uses it without comment. For example, in the case of sets, the relation is that of set equality; it is a congruence relation on any collection of sets. If one is attempting to demonstrate that a particular system $\mathfrak{C}$ has properties B_1–B_4, he will interpret the occurrences of the equality sign in these as the natural equality for $\mathfrak{C}$. For example, in the verification that $\langle \mathscr{P}(X), \cap, ' \rangle$ is a Boolean algebra, " $=$ " will be taken to denote set equality. In summary, the equality symbol, as used in B_1–B_4 need have no absolute nature, but merely a relative one. It suffices that it stand for some congruence relation.

We return to the general discussion with the remark that when one is studying any specific mathematical system $\langle X, \cdots \rangle$ there are often compelling reasons for identifying elements of X which are distinct relative to the natural congruence relation. This amounts to the introduction of an equivalence relation ρ other than the natural one. One then directs his attention to X/ρ, whose elements are the ρ-equivalence classes, and regards it as the basic set. If ρ is not merely an equivalence but a congruence relation, then it is possible to introduce into X/ρ faithful analogues of whatever operations and relations are defined for X. We proceed to discuss this matter in detail for the case of Boolean algebras.

Let $\langle B, \cap, ' \rangle$ be a Boolean algebra, and let θ be a **congruence relation** on it; that is, let θ be an equivalence relation on B such that the following hold:

(C_1) If $a\,\theta\,b$, then $a \cap c\,\theta\,b \cap c$ for all c.

(C_2) If $a\,\theta\,b$, then $a'\,\theta\,b'$.

Further, we agree to exclude, once and for all, the trivial congruence relation which relates every pair of elements of B. We now derive from (C_1) an instance of the earlier substitutivity property (S).

(C_3) If $a \theta c$ and $b \theta d$, then $a \cap b \theta c \cap d$.

For proof, assume that $a \theta c$ and $b \theta d$. Then $a \cap b \theta c \cap b$ and $b \cap c \theta d \cap c$, by (C_1). Since the meet operation is commutative and θ is transitive, the result follows. The derivation of the dual of (C_3) is left as an exercise. If B/θ is the set of θ-equivalence classes $\bar{a}$, then in B/θ the foregoing result (C_3) becomes the following.

$$\text{If } \bar{a} = \bar{c} \text{ and } \bar{b} = \bar{d}, \text{ then } \overline{a \cap b} = \overline{c \cap d}.$$

This means that the relation

$$\{\langle\langle \bar{a},\bar{b}\rangle, \overline{a \cap b}\rangle | \bar{a} \in B/\theta \text{ and } \bar{b} \in B/\theta\}$$

is a function on $(B/\theta) \times (B/\theta)$ into B/θ, that is, an operation in B/θ. We shall denote this operation in B/θ by $\cap$ and its value at $\langle \bar{a},\bar{b}\rangle$ by $\bar{a} \cap \bar{b}$. So, by definition,

$$\bar{a} \cap \bar{b} = \overline{a \cap b}.$$

Next, it follows directly from (C_2) that if $\bar{a} = \bar{b}$, then $\overline{a'} = \overline{b'}$. Hence, the relation $\{\langle \bar{a},\overline{a'}\rangle | \bar{a} \in B/\theta\}$ is a function on B/θ into B/θ. We denote this function by $'$ and its value at $\bar{a}$ by $\bar{a}'$. So, by definition,

$$\bar{a}' = \overline{a'}.$$

It is a straightforward exercise to verify that $\langle B/\theta, \cap, '\rangle$ is a Boolean algebra. For example, to verify B_3, assume that $\bar{a} \cap \bar{b}' = \bar{c} \cap \bar{c}'$. Then, in turn,

$\bar{a} \cap \overline{b'} = \bar{c} \cap \overline{c'},$	by definition of $\bar{x}'$;
$\overline{a \cap b'} = \overline{c \cap c'},$	by definition of $\bar{x} \cap \bar{y}$;
$a \cap b' \theta c \cap c',$	$x \theta y$ iff $\bar{x} = \bar{y}$;
$(a \cap b')' \theta (c \cap c')',$	by (C_2);
$a' \cup b \theta 1,$	by property of $\langle B, \cap, '\rangle$;
$(a' \cup b) \cap a \theta 1 \cap a,$	by (C_1);
$a \cap b \theta a,$	by property of $\langle B, \cap, '\rangle$;
$\overline{a \cap b} = \bar{a},$	$\bar{x} = \bar{y}$ iff $x \theta y$;
$\bar{a} \cap \bar{b} = \bar{a},$	by definition of $\bar{x} \cap \bar{y}$.

In summary, we have shown that from a Boolean algebra $\langle B, \cap, '\rangle$ and a congruence relation θ on it one may derive a Boolean algebra $\langle B/\theta, \cap, '\rangle$ whose elements are θ-equivalence classes and whose operations are defined in terms of those of the original algebra using representatives of equivalence classes. If θ is different from the equality relation in B, the derived algebra may be essentially different from the parent algebra. The relationship of the former to the latter is described following the example below.

EXAMPLE

Consider the Boolean algebra $\langle \mathcal{P}(\mathbf{Z}), \cap, ' \rangle$ whose elements are the subsets of $\mathbf{Z}$, the set of integers. We recall the definition of the symmetric difference, $A + B$, of two sets as the set of all objects which are in one of A and B but not both. For A and B in $\mathcal{P}(\mathbf{Z})$ let us define $A \, \theta \, B$ to mean that $A + B$ has a finite number of elements. It is easily verified that θ is an equivalence relation on $\mathcal{P}(\mathbf{Z})$. Further, if $A \, \theta \, B$, then $A \cap C \, \theta \, B \cap C$, since, for all A, B, and C,

$$(A \cap C) + (B \cap C) = (A + B) \cap C,$$

and, hence, if $A + B$ is finite, then so is $(A \cap C) + (B \cap C)$. Finally, if $A \, \theta \, B$, then $A' \, \theta \, B'$, since $A + B = A' + B'$. Thus, θ is a congruence relation on the given algebra, and a new Boolean algebra whose elements are θ-equivalence classes results on defining

$$\overline{A} \cap \overline{B} = \overline{A \cap B} \text{ and } \overline{A'} = \overline{A}'.$$

That a substantial collapse of elements has taken place on transition from the first to the second algebra is indicated by the fact that, in the first the zero element is $\varnothing$, whereas in the second the zero element, $\overline{\varnothing}$, is the family of all finite subsets of $\mathbf{Z}$.

At this point it becomes desirable to simplify our notation by identifying an algebra simply by its basic set. Thus, we shall use the phrase "the Boolean algebra B" in place of "the Boolean algebra $\langle B, \cap, ' \rangle$." Let us consider now the relationship of a Boolean algebra B/θ to the algebra B from which B/θ is derived using a congruence relation. Let p be the natural mapping (see Section 1.9) on the *set* B onto the *set* B/θ, that is, the mapping

$$p: B \to B/\theta, \text{ where } p(b) = \overline{b}.$$

Since $\overline{a} \cap \overline{b} = \overline{a \cap b}$ and $\overline{a}' = \overline{a'}$,

$$p(a \cap b) = p(a) \cap p(b) \text{ and } p(a') = (p(a))'.$$

That is, p is a "many-to-one" mapping (unless θ is the equality relation in B) which preserves operations. A mapping on one Boolean algebra, B, onto another, C, which takes meets into meets and complements into complements, is a **homomorphism**, and C is a **homomorphic image** of B. The concept of homomorphism generalizes that of isomorphism (see Section 3.3) and, like isomorphism, is defined separately for each type of mathematical system. Returning to the case at hand, we may say that p is a homomorphism and B/θ is a homomorphic image of B. That is, each congruence relation on a Boolean algebra determines a homomorphic image. Conversely, each homomorphic image C of a Boolean algebra B determines a congruence relation on B. Indeed, if $f: B \to C$ is a homomorphism, then the relation θ defined by $a\,\theta\,b$ iff $f(a) = f(b)$ is a congruence relation on B. The proof is left as an exercise. We continue by showing that B/θ, the algebra of θ-equivalence classes, is isomorphic to C. For this we introduce the relation g, which is defined to be

$$\{\langle \bar{x}, f(x)\rangle | \bar{x} \in B/\theta\}.$$

It is easily seen that g is a function which maps B/θ onto C in a one-to-one fashion and that

$$g(\bar{x} \cap \bar{y}) = g(\overline{x \cap y}) = f(x \cap y) = f(x) \cap f(y) = g(\bar{x}) \cap g(\bar{y}),$$
$$g(\bar{x}') = g(\overline{x'}) = f(x') = (f(x))' = (g(\bar{x}))',$$

that is, g is an isomorphism. Moreover, if p is the natural mapping on B onto B/θ, then we observe that for the given homomorphism $f: B \to C$ we have $f = g \circ p$. The next theorem summarizes our results.

THEOREM 4.4.   Let B be a Boolean algebra and θ be a congruence relation on B. Then the algebra B/θ of θ-equivalence classes is a homomorphic image of B under the natural mapping on B onto B/θ. Conversely, if the algebra C is a homomorphic image of B, then C is isomorphic to some B/θ. Moreover, if $f: B \to C$ is the homomorphism at hand, then $f = g \circ p$, where p is the natural mapping on B onto B/θ and g is an isomorphism of B/θ with C.

It should be clear from the foregoing results that the homomorphisms of a Boolean algebra are in one-to-one correspondence with the congruence relations on the algebra. The importance of the role which congruence relations play suggests the problem of practical ways to generate them. One way is provided by a distinguished type of subset of a Boolean algebra which we define next. A nonempty subset I of a Boolean algebra B is an **ideal** iff

(i) $x \in I$ and $y \in I$ imply $x \cup y \in I$, and

(ii) $x \in I$ and $y \in B$ imply $x \cap y \in I$.

For example, if $a \in B$, then $\{x \in B | x \leq a\}$ is an ideal; this is the **principal ideal** generated by a, symbolized (a). To show that (a) is an ideal, we note that if $x \in (a)$ and $y \in (a)$, then a is an upper bound of $\{x,y\}$ and, consequently, is greater than or equal to $x \cup y$, the least upper bound of x and y (see Theorem 4.2). Thus, $x \cup y \in (a)$. Finally, if $x \in (a)$ and $y \in B$, then $x \cap y \leq a$, since $x \leq a$. Two trivial ideals of B, namely, $\{0\}$ and B, are both principal; indeed, $\{0\} = (0)$, and $B = (1)$. The ideal (0) is the **zero ideal,** and the ideal (1) is the **unit ideal** of B. The relationship between ideals of B and congruence relations on B is given in the following theorem.

THEOREM 4.5.   Let B be a Boolean algebra and θ be a congruence relation on B. Then $I = \{x \in B | x \, \theta \, 0\}$ is an ideal of B different from B, and $x \, \theta \, y$ iff there exists an element t in I such that $x \cup t = y \cup t$. Conversely, if I is any ideal of B different from B, then the relation θ on B, given by $x \, \theta \, y$ iff there exists a t in I such that $x \cup t = y \cup t$, is a congruence relation on B such that I is the set of elements congruent to 0. Thus, the congruence relations on B are in one-to-one correspondence with the ideals of B which are different from B; each θ corresponds to the ideal I of elements congruent to 0.

Proof.   The case of the ideal B of B leads to the universal relation on B, which we have excluded from the congruence relations on B. We leave the details of this extreme situation to the reader and discuss only the nontrivial case.

Let θ be a congruence relation on B and let I be defined as stated. Then $\{0\} \subset I \subset B$ and, if $x \in I$ and $y \in I$, then, in turn,

$$x \, \theta \, 0, \; x' \, \theta \, 1, \; x' \cap y' \, \theta \, 1 \cap y', \; x' \cap y' \, \theta \, y', \; x \cup y \, \theta \, y.$$

The last fact, when combined with $y \, \theta \, 0$, implies that $x \cup y \, \theta \, 0$, which proves that I satisfies the first of the defining conditions for an ideal. Next, let $x \in I$ and $y \in B$. Since $x \, \theta \, 0$ implies $x \cap y \, \theta \, 0$, the second condition is satisfied, and I is an ideal.

Now assume that $x \cup t = y \cup t$ for some t in I. From $t \, \theta \, 0$ we infer that $x \cup t \, \theta \, x$, $y \cup t \, \theta \, y$, and, hence, that $x \, \theta \, y$. Conversely, assume that $x \, \theta \, y$, and form $t = (x \cap y') \cup (x' \cap y)$. Then $x \cup t = x \cup y = y \cup t$. Further, $t \, \theta \, 0$, since $x \, \theta \, y$ implies that $x \cap y' \, \theta \, 0$ and $x' \cap y \, \theta \, 0$, whence $t \, \theta \, 0$.

To prove the converse, let I be an ideal of B, and define the relation θ as stated in the theorem. Clearly, θ is reflexive and symmetric. It is transitive, since if $x \cup t = y \cup t$ and $y \cup u = z \cup u$, with $t \in I$ and $u \in I$, then

$$x \cup (t \cup u) = y \cup t \cup u = y \cup u \cup t = z \cup u \cup t = z \cup (t \cup u),$$

which means that $x \, \theta \, z$, since $t \cup u \in I$. Hence, θ is an equivalence relation. Next we prove that if $x \, \theta \, y$, then $x \cap z \, \theta \, y \cap z$. Let $x \, \theta \, y$. Then $x \cup t = y \cup t$ for $t \in I$, and

$$(x \cap z) \cup t = (x \cup t) \cap (z \cup t) = (y \cup t) \cap (z \cup t) = (y \cap z) \cup t.$$

Therefore, $x \cap z \, \theta \, y \cap z$. Finally, we prove that if $x \, \theta \, y$, then $x' \, \theta \, y'$. Assume that $x \, \theta \, y$. Then $x \cup t = y \cup t$, where $t \in I$. Hence, in turn,

$$x' \cap t' = y' \cap t', (x' \cap t') \cup t = (y' \cap t') \cup t,$$
$$(x' \cup t) \cap 1 = (y' \cup t) \cap 1,$$

or, in other words, $x' \cup t = y' \cup t$. Thus, $x' \, \theta \, y'$.

We complete the proof of the converse by proving that $x \, \theta \, 0$ iff $x \in I$. Assume that $x \, \theta \, 0$. Then $x \cup t = t$ for $t \in I$. Hence, $x \cap t = x$, and so $x \in I$. The identity $x \cup x = x$ yields the converse.

In conclusion we note that from the two preceding theorems there follows the existence of a one-to-one correspondence between the homomorphisms of a Boolean algebra B and those ideals of B which are different from B.

EXERCISES

1. Prove the dual of property (C_3) for a congruence relation θ, namely,

$(C_3)'$ If $a \, \theta \, c$ and $b \, \theta \, d$, then $a \cup b \, \theta \, c \cup d$.

2. Complete the proof of the assertion in the text that $\langle B/\theta, \cap, ' \rangle$ is a Boolean algebra if $\langle B, \cap, ' \rangle$ is a Boolean algebra and θ is a congruence relation on B.

3. Prove the assertion prior to Theorem 4.4 that if $f: B \to C$ is a homomorphism, then the relation θ defined by $a \, \theta \, b$ iff $f(a) = f(b)$ is a

congruence relation on the Boolean algebra B. Further, prove that $f = g \circ p$, where g and p are the mappings defined in the text.

4. Draw the diagram of the algebra $\mathcal{C}$ of all subsets of $\{a,b,c,d\}$. Locate the members of the ideal $(\{a\})$ on the diagram. Then use the diagram to determine the θ-equivalence classes, where θ is the congruence relation determined by $(\{a\})$ in accordance with Theorem 4.5. Finally, draw the diagram of the homomorphic image $\mathcal{C}/\theta$ of $\mathcal{C}$.

5. Justify the assertion in the text that the homomorphisms of a Boolean algebra are in one-to-one correspondence with its congruence relations.

6. Referring to the Example in this section, supply proofs of the steps which culminate in the assertion that θ is a congruence relation on $\mathcal{P}(\underline{Z})$.

7. In the next section an atom of a Boolean algebra is defined to be nonzero element a such that if $b \leq a$, then either $b = 0$ or $b = a$. Show that there are no atoms in the Boolean algebra of equivalence classes defined in the Example in this section.

8. Referring again to the Example in this section, let $A \, \theta_1 \, B$ mean that $A \, \theta \, B$ and that 3 is not a member of $A + B$. Prove that θ_1 is a congruence relation on $\mathcal{P}(\underline{Z})$. Determine the atoms of $\mathcal{P}(\underline{Z})/\theta_1$.

4.5. Representations of Boolean Algebras

The set-theoretical analogue of our second formulation of the theory of Boolean algebras is that of an algebra of sets. Since it was essentially the structure of such a system that motivated the creation of the axiomatic theory under discussion, an obvious representation problem arises: Is every Boolean algebra isomorphic to an algebra of sets? This we can answer in the affirmative.

We shall begin with the case where the set B has a finite number of elements, although our first definition is applicable to any Boolean algebra. An element a of a Boolean algebra is an **atom** iff $a \neq 0$ and $b \leq a$ implies that either $b = 0$ or $b = a$. For x in B let $A(x)$ denote the set of all atoms such that $a \leq x$. We next derive several properties of atoms and of the sets $A(x)$ for the case of an algebra $\langle B, \cap, ' \rangle$ such that B is finite.

A_1.   If $x \neq 0$, there exists an atom a with $a \leq x$.

Proof. This is a direct consequence of the finiteness assumption. The details are left as an exercise.

A₂. If a is an atom and $x \in B$, then exactly one of $a \leq x$ and $a \cap x = 0$ holds. Alternatively, exactly one of $a \leq x$ and $a \leq x'$ holds.

Proof. Since $a \cap x \leq a$, either $a \cap x = a$ or $a \cap x = 0$. Moreover, both cannot hold, since $a \neq 0$.

A₃. $A(x \cap y) = A(x) \cap A(y)$.

Proof. First we note that $x \cap y$ is the meet of two elements in B, and $A(x) \cap A(y)$ is the set of those elements common to $A(x)$ and $A(y)$. Now, assume that $a \in A(x \cap y)$. Then $a \leq x \cap y$, and, hence, $a \leq x$ and $a \leq y$. Thus $a \in A(x) \cap A(y)$. Hence, $A(x \cap y) \subseteq A(x) \cap A(y)$. Reversing the foregoing steps establishes the reverse inequality, and, hence, equality.

A₄. $A(x') = A(1) - A(x)$.

Proof. First we note that $A(1)$ is the set of all atoms of B. Now let $a \in A(x')$. Then, by A₂, it is false that $a \in A(x)$. Hence, $a \in A(1) - A(x)$. Conversely, if $a \in A(1) - A(x)$, then $a \notin A(x)$. Hence, by A₂, $a \in A(x')$.

A₅. $A(x) = A(y)$ iff $x = y$.

Proof. Assume $x \neq y$. Then at least one of $x \leq y$ and $y \leq x$ is false. Suppose that $x \leq y$ is false. Then $x \cap y' \neq 0$, so that by A₁ there exists an atom $a \leq x \cap y'$. By A₃, $a \in A(x)$ and $a \in A(y')$. Thus, $a \in A(x)$ and, by A₄, $a \notin A(y)$. Hence, $A(x) \neq A(y)$. The same conclusion follows similarly if it is assumed that $y \leq x$ is false.

A₆. If $a_1, a_2, \cdots, a_k$ are distinct atoms, $A(a_1 \cup a_2 \cup \cdots \cup a_k) = \{a_1, a_2, \cdots, a_k\}$.

Proof. Clearly, $\{a_1, a_2, \cdots, a_k\} \subseteq A(a_1 \cup a_2 \cup \cdots \cup a_k)$. For the converse, assume that $a \in A(a_1 \cup a_2 \cup \cdots \cup a_k)$ and $a \neq a_i$, $i = 1$, $2, \cdots k$. Then, by A₂, $a \cap a_i = 0$, $i = 1, 2, \cdots, k$, and, hence, $a = a \cap (a_1 \cup a_2 \cup \cdots \cup a_k) = (a \cap a_1) \cup (a \cap a_2) \cup \cdots \cup (a \cap a_k) = 0$, which is impossible.

THEOREM 4.6. Let B be a Boolean algebra of n elements. Then B is isomorphic to the algebra of all subsets of the set of atoms of B. If m is the number of atoms of B, then $n = 2^m$.

Proof.   Let B^* be the power set of $\{a_1, a_2, \cdots, a_m\}$, the set of atoms of B. Then $f: B \rightarrow B^*$, where $f(x) = A(x)$ is one-to-one, by A_5, and onto B^*, by A_6. According to A_3, the image of a meet in B is the meet of the corresponding images in B^*. According to A_4, the image $A(x')$ of x' is the complement of the image of x, that is, the relative complement of $A(x)$ in the set of atoms. Thus, f is an isomorphism.

Then $n = 2^m$ follows from the fact established earlier that the power set of a set of m elements has 2^m members.

COROLLARY.   Two Boolean algebras with the same finite number of elements are isomorphic.

Proof.   This is left as an exercise.

EXAMPLE

For B we choose $\{1,2,3,5,6,10,15,30\}$, the set of divisors of 30. For a and b in B define $a \cap b$ as the least common multiple of a and b and a' as $30/a$. It is an easy matter to verify that $\langle B, \cap, ' \rangle$ is a Boolean algebra. The partial ordering relation introduced for the elements of a Boolean algebra takes the following form for this algebra: $a \leq b$ iff a is a multiple of b. Thus, 30 is the least (and, zero) element, and 1 is the greatest (and, unit) element of the algebra. The atoms are 6, 10, and 15, and, consequently, the algebra is isomorphic to that determined by all subsets of $\{6,10,15\}$ with the usual operations. The mapping which establishes this isomorphism matches 2 with $\{6,10\}$ and 30 with $\varnothing$, for example. It is left as an exercise to verify that $a \cup b$, which in our second formulation of a Boolean algebra is defined as $(a' \cap b')'$, is the greatest common divisor of a and b. Thus, if at the outset we had introduced in B, along with the operation $\cap$, a second binary operation $\cup$ by defining $a \cup b$ as the greatest common divisor of a and b, the outcome would have been the same. However, in the process, we would have had had to verify the distributive laws, which, in this case, is not a particularly simple matter.

Before continuing with the representation theory we urge the reader to pause and reflect on the extent to which Theorem 4.6 clarifies the structure of *finite* Boolean algebras (that is, algebras having a finite number of elements). Indeed, it leaves nothing to be desired in the way of a representation theorem. Possibly its definiteness, both with respect to its arithmetical aspect and the inclusion of an explicit recipe for constructing the asserted isomorphism, will be more fully appreciated when the corresponding result for the infinite case is obtained. For this a different approach must be supplied, since there exist Boolean algebras without atoms (see Exercise 7, Section 4.4). In the infinite case the substitute for an atom is a distinguished type of ideal, which we describe next. Let S be the set of all ideals different from B in the Boolean algebra B. Since $\{0\} \in S$, it is nonempty. Further, the members of S may be characterized as the ideals of B which do not contain 1. As is true of any collection of sets, S is partially ordered by the inclusion relation, and the concept of a maximal element of S is defined. A maximal element of S is a **maximal ideal** of B. The existence of maximal ideals in an infinite Boolean algebra is secured by an application of the third and last assumption of intuitive set theory. That is, this assumption has the same status as the principles of set extension and abstraction which were introduced in Section 1.2. A variety of equivalent formulations are known for it, and some of these have well-established names (for example, "the axiom of choice" and "the well-ordering theorem"). It suits our needs best to state it in the form known as "Zorn's lemma." To understand it, the reader may have to reread that part of Section 1.10 which follows Theorem 1.7.

Zorn's lemma. *A partially ordered set, each of whose simply ordered subsets has an upper bound, contains a maximal element.*

THEOREM 4.7. Maximal ideals of a Boolean algebra exist. Indeed, there exists a maximal ideal which includes any preassigned ideal different from B.

Proof. We consider the partially ordered set $\langle S, \subseteq \rangle$ defined above. If $\mathcal{C}$ is a simply ordered subset of S, then $A = \{x \in B \mid$ for some I in $\mathcal{C}, x \in I\}$ is clearly an upper bound for $\mathcal{C}$. It is a straightforward exercise to verify that A is an ideal. Moreover, $A \in S$, since 1 appears in no member of $\mathcal{C}$ and, consequently, does not appear in A. Thus, since every chain in S has an upper bound in S, Zorn's lemma may be applied to conclude the existence of a maximal element. The same argument when applied to $\{I \in S \mid I \supseteq J\}$, where J is a given ideal different from B, yields the existence of a maximal element which includes J.

We prove next a sequence of theorems about maximal ideals of a Boolean algebra B which closely parallels that derived earlier for atoms.

M_1. If $x \neq 1$, there exists a maximal ideal P with $P \supseteq (x)$ or, what amounts to the same, $x \in P$.

Proof. This follows directly from the final statement of Theorem 4.7, choosing (x) as the given ideal.

M_2. For each maximal ideal P and each element x of B, exactly one of $x \in P$ and $x' \in P$ holds.

Proof. We note first that for no x is $x \in P$ and $x' \in P$, since it would then follow that $1 (= x \cup x') \in P$, which is impossible. Now assume that $x \notin P$, and consider the set Q of all elements of B of the form $b \cup p$ with $b \leq x$ and $p \in P$. Then Q is an ideal, since

(i) $(b_1 \cup p) \cup (b_2 \cup p) = (b_1 \cup b_2) \cup (p_1 \cup p_2) = b_3 \cup p_3$, and

(ii) if $y \in B$, then $(b \cup p) \cap y = (b \cap y) \cup (p \cap y) = b_1 \cup p_1$.

Also, $P \subset Q$, since, clearly, $P \subseteq Q$ and $x \in Q$, while $x \notin P$. Thus, $Q = B$, since P is maximal. Hence, for some $b \leq x$ and $p \in P$, $b \cup p = 1$. It follows that $x \cup (b \cup p) = x \cup 1$, or $x \cup p = 1$. Then

$$x' = x' \cap 1 = x' \cap (x \cup p) = (x' \cap x) \cup (x' \cap p) = x' \cap p.$$

By the second part of the definition of an ideal it follows that $x' \in P$.

To continue with the derivation of properties of maximal ideals which parallel, in a complementary sort of way, those for atoms, we introduce the analogue of the sets $A(x)$. If $x \in B$, let $M(x)$ be the set of all maximal ideals P such that $x \notin P$ or, what amounts to the same by virtue of M_2, $x' \in P$. The sets $M(x)$ have the following properties.

M_3. $M(x \cap y) = M(x) \cap M(y)$.

Proof. Let $P \in M(x \cap y)$. Then $(x \cap y)' = x' \cup y' \in P$. Since $x' = x' \cap (x' \cup y')$ and $y' = y' \cap (x' \cup y')$, it follows that $x' \in P$ and $y' \in P$. Hence $P \in M(x)$ and $P \in M(y)$, or $P \in M(x) \cap M(y)$. Since each of these steps is reversible, the asserted equality follows.

M_4. $M(x') = M(1) - M(x)$, where $M(1)$ is the set of all maximal ideals of the algebra.

Proof. We have $P \in M(x')$ iff $x' \notin P$ iff $x \in P$ iff $P \in M(1) - M(x)$.

M_5. $M(x) = M(y)$ iff $x = y$.

Proof. Assume $x \neq y$. Then at least one of $x \leq y$ and $y \leq x$ is false. It is sufficient to consider the consequences of one of these. Let us say $y \leq x$ is false. Then $x \cup y' \neq 1$, so there exists a maximal ideal P such that $x \cup y' \in P$. Now $(x \cup y')' = x' \cap y \notin P$, and, hence, by M_3, $P \in M(x')$ and $P \in M(y)$, or $P \notin M(x)$ and $P \in M(y)$. Thus, $M(x) \neq M(y)$.

The promised representation theorem follows easily from M_1–M_5. It is valid for an arbitrary Boolean algebra, but, in view of the more precise result for finite algebras, it is of interest only in the infinite case. The first proof of this result was given in 1936 by the American mathematician, Marshall Stone.

THEOREM 4.8. Every Boolean algebra B is isomorphic to an algebra of sets based on the set of all maximal ideals of B.

Proof. Let $B^* = \{M(x) | x \in B\}$. According to M_3, if $M(x)$ and $M(y)$ are members of B^*, then so is their intersection. According to M_4, if $M(x) \in B^*$, then the complement of $M(x)$ in $M(1)$ is a member of B^*. Thus B^* is an algebra of sets. The mapping $f: B \to B^*$, where $f(x) = M(x)$, is onto, by definition of B^*, and one-to-one, by M_5. According to M_3 and M_4, it preserves intersections and complements. Thus $\langle B, \cap, ' \rangle$ and $\langle B^*, \cap, ' \rangle$ are isomorphic.

With the representation theorem for the finite case in mind, it is natural to inquire whether the above theorem cannot be sharpened to read "Every Boolean algebra is isomorphic to the algebra of all subsets of some base set." On reflection the reader should be able to convince himself that a prerequisite for this is that the Boolean algebra be **atomic**, that is, have the property that for each nonzero element b there exist an atom a with $a \leq b$. The reader has already been asked to verify that the algebra described at the end of Section 4.4 has no atoms. So this algebra is not atomic, and the matter is thereby settled. Necessary and sufficient conditions that a Boolean algebra be isomorphic to the algebra of subsets of some set have been found. The following is one such list of conditions. The algebra $\langle B, \cap, ' \rangle$ must be atomic, **complete** (that is, for every nonempty subset A of B, lub A exists relative to the partial ordering for B), and **distributive** (that is, for every subset A of B such that lub A exists, and for every element b of B,

$b \cap (\text{lub } A) = \text{lub } \{b \cap a | a \in A\}$). A Boolean algebra satisfying these conditions is isomorphic to the algebra of all subsets of the set of atoms. We shall not prove this result.

EXERCISES

1. Prove A_1.

2. Prove the Corollary to Theorem 4.6.

3. Referring to the Example in this section, verify that the divisors of 30 determine a Boolean algebra. Verify that in this algebra $a \cup b$ is the greatest common divisor of a and b.

4. Referring to the same Example, show that the set of divisors of any square-free integer n determines a Boolean algebra in exactly the same way as to the divisors of 30.

5. Referring to the preceding exercise, state and prove a theorem concerning the number of divisors of a square-free integer.

4.6. Statement Calculi as Boolean Algebras

Statement calculi, as described in Section 2.3, yield models of the theory of Boolean algebras. One need merely restrict his attention to the algebraic character of a statement calculus as we now discuss it.

According to Section 2.3, the core of a statement calculus is a non-empty set S_0 of statements. This set is extended to the smallest set S of statements (that is, formulas) such that the negation of each member of S is a member of S and each of the conjunction, disjunction, conditional, and biconditional of any two members of S is a member of S. Since it was agreed that two members of S would be regarded as indistinguishable if they yielded equal truth functions (this is the eq-relation for formulas), and since it was shown that each formula is equivalent to one involving no connectives other than "not" and "and," we may and shall assume that S is simply the closure of S_0 with respect to these connectives. Then, $\wedge$ takes on the role of a binary operation in S and ′ (which we shall use as the symbol for negation) that of a unary operation in S.

In order to state precisely the structure of the system $\langle S, \wedge, ' \rangle$, that is, the set S together with its two operations, we must decide on the "natural" congruence relation for it. The obvious choice is the eq-relation. With the adoption of eq as the equality relation on S we assert that $\langle S, \wedge, ' \rangle$ is a Boolean algebra. For proof we note first that eq is a congruence relation for the system. Indeed, we already know that it is an equivalence relation and, using truth tables, it is an easy matter to prove that A eq B implies that $(A \wedge C)$ eq $(B \wedge C)$ and A' eq B'. Moreover, it is a straightforward exercise to verify that B_1–B_4 of Theorem 4.3 are satisfied; that is, $(A \wedge B)$ eq $(B \wedge A)$, and so on. The zero element of the Boolean algebra $\langle S, \wedge, ' \rangle$ is $A \wedge A'$ for any formula A, and the unit element is $(A \wedge A')'$. Frequently the result which we have obtained is stated as "The statement calculus under the connectives 'and' and 'not' is a Boolean algebra." This is somewhat misleading, since there is a statement calculus for each set S_0. Actually, it is only the size of S_0 that matters (regarding two sets as having the same size if there exists a one-to-one correspondence between them); two calculi for which the respective sets of basic statements have the same size differ only in verbal foliage. Thus, a more accurate assertion, in the sense that it recognizes the existence of different statement calculi and the congruence relation employed, is "A statement calculus under the connectives 'and' and 'not' is a Boolean algebra with respect to equivalence." Such systems provide models of the theory of Boolean algebras which are substantially different from algebras of sets (superficially, at least).

4.7. Free Boolean Algebras

The preceding section provides the genesis of a method for constructing, in a purely formal way, a Boolean algebra from any nonempty set. This involves the use of congruence relations in a way which extends that described in Section 4.4. Let us dispose of this matter first.

In Section 4.4 the rough assertion was made that if $\langle X, \cdots \rangle$ is a mathematical system and ρ is a congruence relation for it, then, corresponding to each operation (or relation) in X, there can be defined in X/ρ an operation (or relation) having all of the properties of the original. (This was stated precisely and proved in the case of a Boolean algebra.) Now it can happen that the resulting system with X/ρ as basic set has additional properties besides those inherited from the original system. Intuitively, this seems quite plausible; if X is collapsed appropriately, irregular behavior present in the original system may be smoothed out in the derived one. An instance of this occurs below;

a system which has some requisites of a Boolean algebra is forced into determining one by introducing a suitable congruence relation.

The system with which we begin is the abstraction of the most obvious features of an intuitive statement calculus. We proceed with its definition. Let S_0 be an arbitrary nonempty set and $\wedge$ and $'$ be two symbols which do not designate elements of S_0. We give an inductive definition of a set S whose elements are certain finite sequences of elements of $S_0 \cup \{\wedge,'\}$ together with parentheses.

   (I) If $s \in S_0$, then $s \in S$.

   (II) If $t \in S$, then $(t)' \in S$.

  (III) If s, $t \in S$, then $(s) \wedge (t) \in S$.

  (IV) The only members of S are those resulting from a finite number of applications of (I), (II), and (III).

As a direct consequence of the definition of S we may regard $\wedge$ as a binary operation in S and $'$ as a unary operation in S. In these formal circumstances the natural congruence relation for the system $\langle S, \wedge, ' \rangle$ is that of elements having identical form. As such, $\langle S, \wedge, ' \rangle$ is surely not a Boolean algebra. Can a congruence relation be defined for the system such that a Boolean algebra will result? On the basis of the discussion in Section 4.4, necessary and sufficient conditions which such a relation θ must satisfy are that it be an equivalence relation different from the universal relation on S (the latter requirement reflects the fact that a Boolean algebra has more than one element) and that the following hold for all elements of S.

      If $s \theta t$, then $s \wedge u \theta t \wedge u$ for all u.†

      If $s \theta t$, then $s' \theta t'$.

(C) $s \wedge t \theta t \wedge s$.

      $s \wedge (t \wedge u) \theta (s \wedge t) \wedge u$.

      If $s \wedge t' \theta u \wedge u'$ for some u, then $s \wedge t \theta s$.

      If $s \wedge t \theta s$, then $s \wedge t' \theta u \wedge u'$ for all u.

That the class $\mathcal{C}$ of such relations θ is nonempty may be shown by interpreting members of S as truth functions of a statement calculus and defining $s \theta t$ (for s, $t \in S$) iff s and t are equal as truth functions.

Consider now the relation μ in S defined as follows: $s \mu t$ iff $s \theta t$ for every θ in $\mathcal{C}$. It is left as an exercise to prove that $\mu \in \mathcal{C}$. This is the

---

† Here we begin to follow the usual mathematical conventions of omitting superfluous parentheses.

least member of the partially ordered set $\langle \mathcal{C}, \subseteq \rangle$ (remember that relations are sets!) in the sense that it relates the fewest possible pairs of elements of S. Since the first two statements in (C) above hold for μ, operations in S/μ are defined by setting

$$\bar{s} \wedge \bar{t} = \overline{s \wedge t} \text{ and } \bar{s}' = \overline{s'}.$$

Since the remaining statements in (C) hold for μ, $\langle S/\mu, \wedge, ' \rangle$ is a Boolean algebra, the so-called **free Boolean algebra** generated by S_0.

It is possible to give an interesting characterization of the congruence relation μ. To this end we introduce the subset V of S defined as follows.

$$V = \{s \in S \mid s \, \mu \, (t \wedge t')' \text{ for some } t \text{ in } S\}.$$

If θ is any member of the set $\mathcal{C}$ of congruence relations, then $(t \wedge t')' \, \theta$ $(u \wedge u')'$ for all t and u in S, and, hence, $(t \wedge t')' \, \mu \, (u \wedge u')'$ for all t and u. It follows that for any t in S, $V = \{s \in S \mid s \, \mu \, (t \wedge t')'\}$. Thus, V is a μ-equivalence class and among its members are all elements of S having the form $(t \wedge t')'$. It is left as an exercise to show further that if s and t are in S, then

$$s \, \mu \, t \text{ iff } (s \wedge t')' \wedge (t \wedge s')' \in V.$$

The above characterization of μ in terms of the subset V of S is hopelessly opaque until S is interpreted as the set of formulas of a statement calculus. Then it will be recognized that μ is to be interpreted as the eq-relation and V as the set of valid formulas. Finally, the characterization of μ in terms of V comes to this: Two formulas s and t are equivalent iff the biconditional $s \leftrightarrow t$ is a valid formula. The suspicion that this interpretation of S motivated the program for the formal system is entirely correct.

The same interpretation of S suggests, as an alternative approach to the definition of the algebra generated by S_0, the introduction of the set V first, followed by the definition of μ in terms of V. This is possible using some formulation of a statement calculus as an axiomatic theory. Let us sketch this approach. The starting point is the inductive definition of the set S in terms of the elements of $S_0 \cup \{\wedge, '\}$, just as before. Now the idea is to define the subset V of S as those elements of S which, in the interpretation of S, are tautologies. For this we call on Section 3.6. Introducing $s \vee t$ and $s \rightarrow t$ as abbreviations for $(s' \wedge t')'$ and $(s \wedge t')'$, respectively, the definition of V is the following.

(I) Any member of S that has one of the following four forms is a member of V:

$$(a \vee a) \to a,$$
$$a \to (a \vee b),$$
$$(a \vee b) \to (b \vee a),$$
$$(a \to b) \to ((c \vee a) \to (c \vee b)).$$

(II) If s and t are members of S such that both s and $s \to t$ are members of V, then t is a member of V.

(III) An element of S is a member of V iff it can be accounted for using (I) and (II).

That the two definitions of the set V are in agreement is precisely the content of the completeness theorem (Theorem 3.3) together with its converse. Starting with the latest definition of V, the relation μ in S may be defined by

$$s \, \mu \, t \text{ iff } (s \to t) \wedge (t \to s) \in V$$

and then shown to coincide with the relation defined earlier.

Turning things around, either of the procedures which culminates in the definition of a free Boolean algebra may be used to define a statement calculus. For example, the system $\langle S, \wedge, ' \rangle$ with μ as the equality relation may be taken as a precise definition of the statement calculus (having a set of the size of S_0 as its basic statements). Also, the μ-equivalence class V may be defined to be the set of valid formulas of S. It is possible to discuss the theory of provability provided by the statement calculus in these terms. Let us suppose that A is a subset of S and that we define μ_A to be the smallest relation in S such that in addition to satisfying the six conditions (C) it satisfies those conditions dictated by A. The effect of the adjunction of A to (C) is to enlarge the congruence μ. This means that a μ_A-equivalence class is the union of several μ-equivalence classes. In particular, the tautologies belong to the same μ_A-equivalence class. An element of this μ_A-equivalence class is a valid consequence of the assumption formulas of A.

With this food for thought we bring to a close our little book on the foundations of mathematics.

EXERCISES

1. Referring to the system $\langle S, \wedge, ' \rangle$ generated from $S_0 \cup \{\wedge, '\}$, show that relation μ, when defined in terms of the family $\mathcal{C}$ of all equivalence relations which satisfy the conditions in (C), is a member of $\mathcal{C}$.

2. Write an expanded version (supplying proofs) of the paragraph in the text wherein the set V is defined in terms of μ and then μ is characterized in terms of V.

3. Let S_0 be a nonempty set. Let S^* be its extension, using the pair $\{\rightarrow,'\}$ in exactly the same way that $\{\wedge,'\}$ are employed in the text to extend S_0 to S. Then $\rightarrow$ is a binary operation in S^*, and $'$ is a unary operation. Define the subset V^* of S^* as follows.

(I) If s, $t \in S^*$, then $(s \rightarrow (t \rightarrow s)) \in V^*$.

(II) If s, t, $u \in S^*$, then $((u \rightarrow (s \rightarrow t)) \rightarrow ((u \rightarrow s) \rightarrow (u \rightarrow t))) \in V^*$.

(III) If s, $t \in S$, then $((s' \rightarrow t') \rightarrow (t \rightarrow s)) \in V^*$.

(IV) If s, $(s \rightarrow t) \in V^*$, then $t \in V^*$.

Show that $\{S^*, V^*\}$ provides an alternative definition of a statement calculus.

References

CHURCH, ALONZO
  Introduction to Mathematical Logic, Princeton University Press, Princeton, N. J., vol. 1, 1956.

FRAENKEL, ABRAHAM A.
  Abstract Set Theory, North Holland Publishing Co., Amsterdam, 1953.

HILBERT, DAVID, AND WILHELM ACKERMAN
  Principles of Mathematical Logic, Chelsea Publishing Co., New York, 1950.

KERSHNER, R. B. AND LEROY R. WILCOX
  The Anatomy of Mathematics, The Ronald Press, New York, 1950.

KLEENE, STEPHEN C.
  Introduction to Metamathematics, D. Van Nostrand Co., Inc., Princeton, N. J., 1952.
  Sets, Logic and Mathematical Foundations, Williams College, Williamstown, Mass., 1956. (Mimeo.)

MARGARIS, ANGELO
  Notes on Mathematical Logic, The Ohio State University, Columbus, Ohio, 1958. (Ditto).

ROSENBLOOM, PAUL C.
  Elements of Mathematical Logic, Dover Publications, New York, 1951.

ROSSER, J. BARKLEY
Logic for Mathematicians, McGraw-Hill Book Co., Inc., New York, 1953.

STABLER, E. RUSSELL
An Introduction to Mathematical Thought, Addison-Wesley Publishing Co., Inc., Reading, Mass., 1953.

TARSKI, ALFRED, ANDRZEJ MOSTOWSKI, AND RAPHAEL M. ROBINSON
Undecidable Theories, Studies in Logic and the Foundations of Mathematics, North Holland Publishing Company, Amsterdam, 1953.

UNIVERSITY OF CHICAGO, COLLEGE MATHEMATICS STAFF
Concepts and Structures of Mathematics, University of Chicago Press, Chicago, 1954.

WILDER, RAYMOND L.
Introduction to the Foundations of Mathematics, John Wiley and Sons, Inc., New York, 1952.

Symbols

202

Index